CONOR McPHERSON

Born in Dublin in 1971, Conor McPherson attended University
College Dublin, where he began to write and direct. He co-founded
the Fly by Night Theatre Company, which performed new plays in
Dublin's fringe venues.

His plays include *Rum and Vodka* (1992), *The Good Thief* (1994),
which won a Stewart Parker Award, and *This Lime Tree Bower*
(1995), which won a Thames TV Award and a Guinness/National
Theatre Ingenuity Award. All three were staged in Dublin by Fly
by Night and published together as *This Lime Tree Bower – Three
Plays*.

In 1996 McPherson became resident writer at the Bush Theatre,
London, where *This Lime Tree Bower* was first seen in Britain that
same year and where *St Nicholas*, commissioned by The Bush, was
given its world premiere in 1997.

A Selection of Other Titles in this Series

*Included in *The Crack in the Emerald: New Irish Drama*
selected and introduced by David Grant

Conor McPherson

ST NICHOLAS
&
THE WEIR

Two Plays

DUBLIN

NEW ISLAND BOOKS

LONDON

NICK HERN BOOKS
in association with the Bush Theatre

A Nick Hern Book/A New Island Book

St Nicholas & The Weir first published as a paperback original
in 1997 in Great Britain by Nick Hern Books, 14 Larden Road,
London W3 7ST in association with the Bush Theatre,
Shepherds Bush Green, London W12 8QD, and in Ireland by
New Island Books, 2 Brookside, Dundrum Road, Dublin 14

Front cover: from a steel engraving by Cruikshank, Leech and
Barham in *The Ingoldsby Legends*

Typeset by Country Setting, Woodchurch, Kent TN26 3TB
Printed and bound in Great Britain by Athenaeum Press Ltd,
Gateshead, Tyne and Wear

New Island Books receives financial assistance from
The Arts Council (An Chomhairle Ealaion), Dublin, Ireland

A CIP catalogue record for this book is available from
the British Library

ISBN 1 85459 347 1 (Nick Hern Books)
      1 874597 58 8 (New Island Books)

Contents

Preface

Christmas for most of us can be very busy. Catching up with friends in pubs for nights on end. It can become like work, like this is your bizarre job. It involves meeting a lot of new people too. Friends of friends. Sometimes it's nice and sometimes it's awkward. Last Christmas I decided to break the ice by telling each new person I met a big lie. And this is it.

I was coming across the Ha'penny bridge today and a seagull blew into my face. It got all tangled up in my glasses and its wings were flapping around my head. People were milling around, trying to help me, and I ended up lying on the ground until they got it free. The seagull was fine and so was I, but as you can imagine, it was very embarrassing.

The first thing people would say after I'd said this was, 'Is that true?' Because although they didn't believe me, we live in a world where we don't expect complete strangers to lie to us. Not in pubs at any rate. But it's nice in the theatre.

St Nicholas is a play performed by one actor. He only plays one character and he doesn't act anything out. He just tells us a story. And for me, that's full of mischief.

When two or more actors talk to each other on stage, it's easy for us to pretend they're not actually in the theatre. If it's good they could be anywhere. Up a mountain, in a football, under the sea, anywhere. But with one actor talking only to the audience, what we have in front of us is a guide. He's telling us about somewhere outside the theatre, not trying to recreate it indoors. The theatre is simply where we meet him. And if it's good we're reminded that we are in the theatre and we like being there.

And that's full of mischief because we collude with the actor in a very direct way. Especially when we have a well known actor in front of us pretending to be someone else in a small theatre. It's a case of 'Who's fooling who here?' And that can be a very rich and liberating experience. Because we've all started playing. It's a very grown-up and well disciplined type of playing, granted, but then so are lots of things. Like making the character a theatre critic.

But just as children's playing is often a rehearsal for adult life and dealings, so our theatrical grown-up playing has its serious intents.

Because we are reflective beings and we like neatness. We want to know what everything *means*. 'What the hell am I supposed *to make* of this?' that's us. That's what makes us responsible. And I think that's what *St Nicholas* might be about. The responsibility reason gives us.

The Weir is an ensemble piece where the actors do talk to each other. It's full of ghost stories. This play was probably inspired by my visits to Leitrim to see my grandad. He lived on his own down a country road in a small house beside the Shannon. I remember him telling me once that it was very important to have the radio on because it gave him the illusion of company. We'd have a drink and sit at the fire. And he'd tell me stories.

And then when you're lying in bed in the pitch black silence of the Irish countryside it's easy for the imagination to run riot. I always felt different there. I can still see him standing on the platform at the station. He always waved for much too long. Much longer than a person who was glad to have their privacy back.

Conor McPherson, January 1997

ST NICHOLAS

For Paddy Breathnach and Robert Walpole
And for Gina

St Nicholas was first performed at the Bush Theatre, London, on 19 February 1997, produced by the Bush Theatre.

Performed by Brian Cox
Directed by Conor McPherson
Lighting by Paul Russell

This play was written while Conor McPherson was attached to the Bush Theatre under the Pearson Television Theatre Writers' Scheme.

A MAN, *late fifties*

A bare stage

Part One

When I was a boy, I was afraid of the dark . . . What was there.

And maybe one of the things I thought was there was vampires.

I don't know. I can't remember now.

But like all of us, whatever idea I did have about them, it was probably all the superstitious bullshit we get in books. And fiction. But that was nothing like the real thing. Like anything, the real thing is a lot more ordinary.

It's a 'matter of fact'. Matter of fact.

And that's far more frightening than anything you can make up.

Because it's real.

It's just there. Casual as everything else. Just waiting to be dealt with.

And there are practical things to be learned. Yes indeed.

Back in those days I was a fat bastard.

And I had a big red mush from drinking.

This is back before 1 met the vampires.

Before I knew what power was and what evil was.

But back then I thought I knew everything.

And I had lots of what I thought power was.

Because I was a theatre critic.

I was a journalist. I was a lucky bastard. I was blessed, or cursed, whichever, with the ability to string words together. I could string words together.

And that's all it was.

I mean, I was intelligent, but I had no real thoughts about things.

I'd never taken the care to form an opinion. I just had them.

And only one care in the world, when I think back on it now, me.

I wanted . . . everything.

Love, I suppose. Respect. Esteem.

But I didn't deserve it. No, I don't think I deserved any respect. But I got it.

Oh yeah. I got it. Because people were afraid of me. I loved it. Going to big productions. Big names.

Careers spanning tens of glittering years.

And everyone afraid of what I'd write ?

Of what I 'liked' ?

And I hardly really liked anything.

And even when I did like something, mostly what I felt was . . . jealous.

I had tried writing.

Tried to convey the feelings I had.

That I genuinely fucking had – for people.

I loved people. I loved the stupid bastards.

But. I had no ideas.

No ideas for a story.

I wanted to let my compassion seep out across the stage.

Handicapped people in love.

Queers and lesbians absolving each other.

A liberal, fucking, all encompassing . . . you know.

But nothing came.

Nothing ever came.

I could only write about what there was already. I was a hack. And I was drunk. I was at gallery openings, milling free glasses of wine. I was in the bar after the premiere of plays.

I was the educated friend of the masses who read me. Protecting them from these artistic charlatans who were trying to rob their money.

And I could feel this . . . light. Going out. I could feel it.

It was panic I suppose.

Getting older, nothing done yet.

I started rows with directors in pubs.

I walked out of plays ten minutes before the end. I was on the telly.

I had all this drive, going nowhere. It was putting me in the ground.

And I'd get a fright you see. And I'd drink. And when I drank I always got vicious hangovers. And I'd be useless. Couldn't do a thing. Just do it again.

And you see, my life was quite conducive to that. There wasn't a problem.

I only needed to get about one solid hour done in a day. And then I was free.

I rehashed columns.

I usually had reviews written before the show was finished.

I could leaf through a current affairs magazine, see something, half an hour, I'd have a thousand words.

Tide me over.

And I was probably in the top five highest paid in the paper. You know? Editors licked the hole off me.

I was a character.

Famous in all the wrong ways. Nobody went without.

Not my fat tracksuit wife.

She didn't want anything.

She was happy enough to get a half bottle of gin into her.

And the days just slipped through her thick fingers.

Big house in the right place.

The cars and the cash. We were a pair of fat fuckers rolling around in the mud.

And our kids.

My girl was at college.

I loved her. I loved her in that way I couldn't look her in the eye, you know? I couldn't find the words.

It was too late. I just left money on the kitchen table every week.

Apparently she was a brilliant student and I suspected she was a writer but I don't think I could have faced it if she was. You know? I avoided her.

I sat in my study with Milton and Chaucer, nice and cosy. And I'd finish a bottle and hit the sack at two or three.

And then I'd hear my boy come in.

He did nothing and I supported it.

All I knew was he stank of deodorant and he had some fruitless ambition to be a musician. Plinking away at that hour of the night.

He didn't want anything to do with me. And even now my face is burning when I think about my children.

And my stomach is like a brick wall.

Well I'd be too drunk to hear my wife snoring for long and I'd lie in the dark with morning coming.

She knew better than to try and touch me. And I would remember that I loved her once, when we were young. We used to sit in her house and everything outside was made for us. All we had to do was keep holding hands. And I couldn't even do that.

No, what I could do was sit in those yellow bars. With the journalists. Men falling in their pints. There was a breed of us, you see, and we weren't mere reporters.

We had columns.

There'd be a gang.

Men and women.

The women just on the verge of going to seed. Just on the brink, you understand.

And I was a big shot in those places. I could've had my pick.

I knew I could.

Those women with buckles on their shoes and their bows all done wrong.

They had each other, those journalists. There were one or two young things in the bloom of youth, but then the responsibility, you see, the responsibility got them. They were expected to have an opinion. On everything.

They were expected to be on top of situations and the current . . . goings on.

Otherwise, what justified their existence?

The man in the street needed to know what to think, hence these objective observers. And that may have partly been their fucking . . . thing.

But the other was the pressure to fill space. Just fill column inches. It's not a pleasant feeling.

You've got to fill it with words.

And these kids could never admit they couldn't find the news. They all used to rob each other.

They'd be dizzy for a year or two. All aflutter with responsibility.

And then all asunder with it.

And then the weight would pile on. Because there was a need for stimulation, wasn't there?

It became more and more that it was easier to stay in town than go home.

A few scoops at tea-time.

And then, time to eat. Money to lose.

And, you fell in with another journalist, as a lover, you were a goner.

Because you'd help each other to keep going. And you'd look at each other with a joyous tear of camaraderie. And then a bawling hatred because well, because you knew this was hell.

Of course it wasn't all like that.

Newspapers wouldn't get printed if it was. There wasn't many of us.

But enough. Enough drunken pig-headedness being passed off as authority.

That's the way I perceived it.

That was the world I was in.

Fuck. You think I was going to surround myself with people who were succeeding?

And what was I like in those places . . .

I wasn't dying, like you might think.

No. I was dead.

And every so often, I get it. I'd smell the rot. And the scotch'd start disappearing fairly fucking sharpish.

Mmm. I was a bollocks to all the other critics.

And I'll tell you why, because it was this: they were all cunts.

Well. I couldn't stand their wishy washiness. They were always looking for an angle. Like children jumping up behind each other to see a parade.

Like the kids filling space.

But most of all I hated them because I wanted them to like me.

But all I was good at was being noticed. The only way I knew how.

By being . . . well, I'd never sit beside another critic.

All that effort being put into being . . . a type of thing.

I had none left for at home.

I would wake up and 'do some work'.

Do an hour.

And my wife would make some lunch for me. And she would sit with me.

She wanted me to say something.

And I could taste her care.

And I'd munch it down.

What are you going to do?

You've got to keep it in, haven't you?

You open those floodgates, Christ knows what the hell is going to come pouring out.

So, it was into town. Stick the head in the office. A few likely recruits.

And a quick jaunt down to wherever the fuck you reckoned you weren't going to be poisoned by the beer.

And I think we took comfort from being in those places.

Where at one time, genius was at work. Or play or . . . Kavanagh, O'Nolan, and what have you.

You know, that it was still possible to produce enduring works even though you were hungover or drunk, even. And then you began to think that it was the only way to produce enduring works.

But, there was nothing noble about those writers waking up at dawn, pissed out of their bins, groping around for the bottle they'd taken home, putting their hand in the puke that had finally let them sleep.

But we'd keep it up . . . all this.

Until nobody really fucking cared any more.

And then I'd shoot off down to the Project or the Peacock to witness another amateur disaster.

And on, and on, and on.

But this was before I met the vampires, Before I worked for them.

Before I had to fight for anything.

It was a girl that got me into trouble.

Unintentionally. It was my fault.

She was an up and coming actress.

I was reviewing a new production of *Salome* at the Abbey.

And when she danced. Fuck me.

I mean, shadows crept about the muscles of her legs. Her arms. Even her fingers had such . . . She was just one more fucking . . . thing beyond my reach.

But I had underestimated my reviewing . . . capacity.

One of my very few moments of modesty.

Back in those days.

It was after the show in the Flowing Tide.

I'd made it for last orders.

My review was already phoned in.

I'd written it on the back of my programme during the show.

Then I rang it in from my car.

And that was the end of that. That was the way I did it.

It was the best of everything.

I could stand there with the cast and ruin their evening. And get paid for it.

I was feeling generous that night.

I gave them a mixed review.

It was twenty past when I got to the pub.

I got two pints and two double Jemmies.

Now I could relax.

I knew Peter Hamilton, the director, from a few years before when I'd been speaking at a symposium on Irish theatre.

He was a prick.

He came over to me.

The cast were mostly in one corner.

I saw the actress who'd played Salome.

Her name was Helen.

I saw her glance over.

Hamilton said he was surprised to see me there. 'Why?' I said.

I had no time for him.

But plenty of time to make that clear, if you know what I mean.

'Were you not reviewing us tonight?' he said. Awful high pitched voice.

I told him the review was gone in and if he nipped over to the paper he could probably get tomorrow's edition.

'Ah, no rush,' he said.

But I could see him getting a little bit restless.

He had no cop.

I knew he was going to give in and ask me. And he did.

'If it's already gone in,' he said, 'you might as well tell me what you thought.'

And then he gave a little laugh like none of this mattered, and he took a big gulp from his pint.

'What I thought.' I said.

I was pretending I'd given it so much consideration it was hard to sum up now.

'Yes,' I said, 'Well I think it's one of the best shows I've seen in years and anybody who knows what's what would be a fool to miss it .'

Well. Hamilton could hardly contain himself. He made the effort to stick around and make a bit of chit chat with me, but as soon as he got the chance he shot off to tell the others.

And that's how the party got going.

A kind of euphoria spread quite quickly and even the barmen didn't seem to want to stop serving.

I got chatting to the cast.

Drinks were placed in front of me.

I even began to believe my own hype. I began to think I had given it a good review.

I was walking around congratulating everybody. 'My life has been changed,' I told them.

They hugged me and I wept.

Why I wept I don't know.

Just an accumulation of drink and aggravated lying, I suppose, but I did.

And it worked and they all thought I was great.

I was different from the other critics who didn't know what they were talking about.

I had a passionate belief in the theatre and what makes it good.

And then we were out in the street and I was tired.

They wanted to go on somewhere else but I knew I was finished.

And anyway it was only a matter of time before someone got their hands on the paper and saw what a lying bastard I was.

I leaned against the car and bid them goodnight.

And off they went.

And then, a cool hand.

Helen.

'I think I'll go home as well,' she said.

I asked her where she lived.

Donnybrook. It was on my way.

Next thing, she was sitting beside me and we were driving through the empty streets.

You know that way?

And I couldn't help taking a sneaky look at her legs.

And I drove fairly slowly.

We didn't talk.

I badly, badly wanted to tell her the truth.

But I wasn't able to.

This was my moment and . . . I may never be that close to her again.

You know?

When we'd stop at the lights and this, I'd be giving her friendly
. . . you know? Smiling at her.

Chaucer and Milton were in the back of the car. Having a great
fucking time.

But this was just a lift home.

Let's not get excited.

Dropped her off in Pembroke Park.

She kissed me on the cheek before she got out. And I was the
lowest thing.

'Good luck tomorrow night,' I said.

And she told me to sleep well.

I couldn't sleep.

I sat in my study with the windows open. That summer breeze.

And I thought about killing myself. I could imagine the cast
reading the review I'd actually given them, talking about what a
complete cunt I was. And then they'd find out I was dead and
they'd feel rotten. That they hadn't taken into account the integrity
you know? The mystery that I was. But I was too chicken for that.

Instead I lay on the sofa and things crawled all over me till it got
bright.

Well. I wasn't the same after that.

The summer, all our prospects, that bright youthful . . .

I was hacking away, reviewing books. On the radio, what have
you.

And I couldn't stop thinking about her. I'd be working and
suddenly I'd remember her and be all . . . fucking hell.

Happy. But that tinge as well.

Wasn't a sexual thing.

If she were ever to give herself to me, it'd be her acceptance of me.
My fat, blotchy skin wasn't the point.

I don't think I even wanted that.

I knew that when we were married, I'd be happy enough just to sit
and watch her tend our beautiful children.

Yeah.

Well the show didn't get any good reviews as it turned out, but the news was it was doing two weeks in London, knocked down from an intended four.

I went back to the Abbey the night it closed.

Broke my fucking heart to watch her.

And I'll tell you, because it was in her arms.

Because you could see her arms working. The weight changing there.

With you and me, it's all this:

We get older, we try to hide the excess. We compensate for our appearance with our 'sense of humour' or our taste, or our . . . mind.

But what if you woke up in the morning and you were the physical specimen you always wanted to be.

Wouldn't that make you happy? Of course it would.

Go a long way in any case.

Because now your smile would beam confidence. Your stride would never need to conceal the way you were built.

And we could all concentrate on just being nice to each other.

This is all getting very nazi now. But Helen had that.

She was never conscious of herself, because everybody else was busy doing that for her. Do you see?

You probably don't.

But that's why when she smiled at you, you knew you were blessed because her will was pure. She had nothing to hide.

Here was this person doing what they wanted, no more and no less.

And to be that thing that she wanted? Well, then you'd stop performing like a fucking monkey.

And that's a peace few of us ever find.

Hmm?

And you could see all that in the assured grace of her arms.

And the way they moved.

And to be in those arms . . .

The next morning I packed a few things. I was going to London.

I left the house like I would any day. My boy was still in bed.

I'd heard him bring a girl in around four and I hadn't heard her leave.

My daughter was gone hours ago.

I wanted to see her before I went.

I was afraid I wasn't going to see her again.

I remembered when she was a little thing.

Crawling into bed beside me on a stormy night.

My hand up the back of her tee-shirt. My hand wider than her back.

Her little feet on my knee.

My wife was out the back doing her flowers.

I watched her for a minute.

She was kneeling with a trowel.

She stopped and pushed her glasses up her nose with the back of her wrist. I didn't feel anything. I just left.

And nothing could have prepared me for the mad . . . fucking . . . things that were going to happen.

That's always the way. It's probably better.

I went to the bank, and then I went to the airport.

I was supposed to be reviewing some lunchtime shite in Bewley's.

And knowing I'd be up in the air by the time it went on, gave me a great, reckless . . .

I was doing something.

There wasn't a cloud in the sky. I was cradled up there.

I think I wanted it to crash.

But then the ground was solid, and this was real.

The air in London was heavy and still. I checked into a hotel and I went for a drink.

I wanted to find out where the cast were staying. Get Helen on her own. Be honest about it. Had to get busy doing this. Had to get busy, and I'll tell you why because I didn't have a clue what the hell I was going to say to her.

I had a day before they arrived for rehearsals.

I did a little bit of relaxing.

Browsed in bookshops.

Sat in pubs. Walked around.

Down the Kings Road, across the Thames, into Battersea. Not the best.

Took the bus back.

I saw the sights.

And I dumped my suit.

It was one I'd had for fifteen years.

Another quirk you see. I was full of that.

Had to get some natty duds. Impress the ladies. Changing in a little cubicle.

Caught myself in the mirror.

Belly like a mountain. Little tits and everything. Suit hid it. But the heat.

Got a linen jacket. And I went drinking.

And back at the hotel, in the early hours,

I took some hotel paper, hotel pen.

Coleridge on my shoulder.

Wrote a poem.

By the time I lay down, there was no paper left. It was all in the bin.

And the big day dawned.

I had a dirty big fry and two pots of tea. Didn't feel like the food of love.

I went down to the theatre, had a walk around.

I saw the scenery go in. And crates.

There was a pub across the road.

I had a quick couple of pints. Back out, walking around. No sign of the cast. Couple more pints.

Thinking about my editor and my wife. Wondering where I was. I'd had binges before. Not to worry, you know? It was that way. Be ringing each other. I never understood why she stayed.

What she saw in me. I couldn't see it.

The cast began to arrive in twos and threes up out of the tube.

But no Helen. She was another hour and a half. Arrived in a taxi. With Peter Hamilton.

What the fuck was this, you know?

She waited for him while he paid the fare. Then she linked his arm and they went inside. I went back in the pub and had a quick double, a bracer.

What were they doing together, you know? Maybe it was nothing.

A little fling at best.

Hamilton abusing his position. He was probably gay anyway.

And theatre people fuck like rabbits. Bucking each other up.

Didn't mean a thing. Nothing.

Compared to what I felt.

Another quick bracer.

At tea time they began to emerge. They were in good form. They were coming into the pub. I lashed out and bought a tweed hat. I pulled it down low and sat in a corner watching them over a newspaper.

Helen was surrounded by men.

It was so obvious. They kept touching her. It was hard to look at.

Finally Hamilton ordered them all to go home about ten.

They had a heavy day tomorrow.

This was it.

Helen left with Hamilton and two other actresses. I followed them.

We all took a tube to Victoria.

They were quiet. They were tired.

We changed trains. Main line.

Out into the suburbs. Out into Kent.

They got out near Bromley.

Went to a little terraced house.

I nipped into a shop, got a cheap bottle of scotch. Needed a bracer for this. I sat on the road and swigged for a little while. Maybe an hour.

And then, when I couldn't feel my heart any more, I went to the house.

They must have been in bed.

Took a while to get an answer.

One of the other actresses, Cliona Leeson, opened the door.

She had a jacket on over her pyjamas. She didn't recognise me with my hat. Peter Hamilton came down behind her, protecting the women.

I took off the hat and offered them the bottle. 'Greetings,' I said.

'Oh my God,' said Hamilton, 'What are you doing here?'

'Just a social call,' I said, 'And I'm looking for the chance to apologise for what my editor did to your review. He was at the show and he didn't agree with me at all.'

Hamilton wasn't sure if this was a dream.

'He changed your review?' he said.

'I'm afraid so,' I said, 'He's always fancied himself. So, naturally, I've resigned from the paper, and here I am. Can I come in?' Hamilton didn't have a choice.

He wasn't the assertive type.

'Just for a minute,' I said, 'I realise it's very late.'

Cliona Leeson yawned and went back upstairs. Left poor Hamilton to deal with this on his own.

He led me into a tiny sitting-room, separated from the kitchen by a counter with stools, for playing at being out.

I made myself comfortable and Hamilton just stood smiling at me. Appalled.

He asked me if I'd like a cup of tea, but I was fine.

He gave me a glass for the scotch.

And I offered him a drink. He needed it. 'I'll tell you, Peter,' I said,' I've decided to come over to spread the word about the fantastic production you've done. The dogs in the street should beat down the doors to see it.'

I was making as much noise as I could, you understand. I was waking the house. Helen would know I'd come for her. And I bellowed.

'What nobody seems to realise, Peter, is that you are probably the foremost director of your generation. But they're fools, aren't they? They're blind! They must be! You're the voice in the wilderness, aren't you?' I heard movement upstairs. Cliona Leeson was telling the others.

They were getting curious.

And I continued my tirade and tore into the bottle. I was even beginning to enjoy myself. But although Hamilton was stupid, he wasn't a complete idiot, and only a complete idiot could fail to see that his work was mediocre at best.

At fucking best, mediocre.

So much as he wanted to believe what I was saying, I was, in fact, making him very miserable.

But I couldn't give a fuck.

I was here to see Helen.

And sure enough, after a while, the girls had worked up their nerve.

There were footsteps on the stairs.

So they had a big day tomorrow. They had to work. But they were on tour, they were open to new experiences.

There may well be a story in all of this.

A famous theatre story.

The critic came to apologise.

Of course they'd come down. And down they came. Three shivering actresses.

Helen looked tired. She didn't look too good. And, when she looked at me, there was nothing,

And my resolve began to crumble, only slightly, but when I told them the review being changed story, I told it falteringly.

And I was running out of things to say about it. I had resigned on their behalf.

On behalf of a production that wouldn't even exist in two weeks.

It sounded like the lie it was.

But I was in for a penny now.

Hamilton wanted to believe me. I think.

It would do his career a world of good.

A critic resigning for his sake. He'd hang on to it.

Cliona Leeson seemed to be amused.

She was smirking into her cup.

Poor Helen looked too exhausted to care. But the third actress, Sheila Kilmeady, she was older. I knew her husband. He did a lot of television. I'd poured a pint over him about ten years before, at a time when I did that sort of thing because it got me the attention I wanted. And I'd brutalised him in the paper for a cameo he did in a British sitcom.

I'd said he was about as funny as wiping your hole with a Brillo pad.

God knows why I picked on him.

But we all need a purpose in life, even if we've got to make it up, ah?

And now, here was his wife, looking at me with all that sage wisdom culchies get when they move to the city and find out that saying smartarse crap for tourists isn't enough anymore. You have to work. And life is hard. And all that shit.

'You seem to have a problem with me taking a stand, Sheila,' I said.

She looked at me for a moment and then she said, 'I just don't believe you, that's all.' And she went to bed.

Nobody said anything. It was all fucked now. Cliona Leeson and Helen followed her. Hamilton told me I was welcome to the couch. I thanked him and then I was on my own. And I realised how pissed I was. I knew I didn't want to be there in the morning. But. Helen. I'd . . . I'd . . . come to . . .

I'd come to say it.

Even if she was like them.

Even if she hated me. I'd come to say it. All I had to do was wait till they were asleep, talk to her on her own.

And maybe, why not? She'd pull back the covers and let me in and . . . Well. I don't know what. First things first. I had to wait.

So I sat there. And I drank. And I dropped off. I didn't dream. It was just black.

I felt something wet and I woke up.

I'd spilled the rest of the whiskey down my pants.

It was a quarter to six.

I stood up and I nearly fell over.

I went to the sink and I puked raw whiskey.

Burned the fucking throat off me.

I needed the toilet, I wasn't well.

It was a near thing getting up the stairs.

I just made it on to the jacks. I had the runs.

I leaned forward with my head in my hands.

And then I saw something.

It was jammed in behind the sink.

I pulled it out. It was a porno mag. Readers' wives. They were in bits. On their living room sofas, legs spread. Arses in the air.

And something lit in me I hadn't felt in a long time.

And I wanted Helen that way.

I wanted to hurt her.

I wanted her to feel it and beg me to stop and beg me to go on.

So I pulled up my pants and I checked the rooms.

It was bright now.

In one room. Hamilton and Cliona Leeson were in bed together. I could see her tits. It spurred me on.

Sheila Shitebag was in the next room with a pillow over her face.

All I had to do was exert a little pressure.

But I had things on my mind.

I pushed Helen's door open slowly.

Sunlight streamed across her bed. I've never seen anything like it.

I wanted to shag her.

All those years I'd sat in my study reading the Elizabethans. I'd forgotten what those poems were about. They were foreplay. They were all about having it off.

I knelt on the bed.

And I couldn't do it.

I couldn't move. Reason had crept into the room behind me and caressed my neck.

This girl. I could only crave her attention, and ruin her.

I was thinking about my girl you see?

I was thinking about something real.

I got up quietly and I left.

The traffic was beginning to thicken.

The first of the commuters.

I was walking west.

Canterbury was in Kent. Where Chaucer sent his pilgrims. Where Christopher Marlowe was born. He was murdered in Kent too.

Wasn't much of that now.

I walked the whole morning.

Had to keep taking a rest.

It was getting hot.

I went up into Crystal Palace Park. Through the long avenues of trees, up to the ruins of Crystal Palace itself. I lay there in the sun and I closed my eyes.

I'd made a total fool of myself.

I couldn't understand how I'd been so stupid as to think anything would have come of this. And I'd fucked myself up as far as Dublin was concerned. Everywhere I went people would laugh. I must have looked like a lunatic.

I was bolloxed.

Chaucer's pilgrims went by.

Christopher Marlowe was arguing about the bill. My daughter climbed into bed beside me. And then someone pulled her out and I heard her screaming.

I woke up. It was dusk.

I was sweating booze.

I was thirsty. Miles from anywhere.

I had to get out of the park before it got too dark to see.

I scratched the gravel out of my hair stood up.

And as I did, I saw something move down by the steps. It was dark and huddled. I thought it was a big dog. I was frightened of dogs. I stood looking. I didn't want to provoke it by moving.

I was going to find another way out of the park. And then, suddenly, it stood up. It was a man.

He looked quite young. Thirty maybe. He started walking towards me.

For a second I thought I was going to be mugged, but there was something about him that made me comfortable.

It was relaxing to watch his easy stride. I just wanted to watch him walk.

As he got nearer I could see he was smiling.

'Beautiful night,' he said.

'Yes,' I said.

He stood beside me and we looked out over the lights of the city.

All those lives.

And then he said, 'Getting dark. We'd want to get back to civilisation.'

'That's a good idea,' I said.

And we began to stroll along.

It was like I'd known him for a long time.

It was natural for us to do this.

Down into the park. Very quiet.

'Were you asleep up there?' he asked me.

'I must have been,' I said, 'Rough night, last night.'

He laughed and said, 'I know what that's like.'

Then he offered me his hand and said,

'My name's William by the way.'

We shook hands. He was cool.

Not cold, like you'd expect a vampire to be.

He was just right. I think I wanted him to touch my face. I wasn't sure. It was getting hard to think. It was easier just to walk.

Interval.

Part Two

They have power. Not the power to make you do what they want.

But real power. To make you want what they want. It hurts to consider things in their company. It becomes hard to make sense. They appeal to the older part of us.

What we share with animals.

That's what they have you see.

So that when William hailed a taxi, I think I got in first.

I'm not sure how far we went.

We stopped on a wide suburban street. Old houses. Imposing pillars.

High trees.

I can still smell the house.

It was damp stones and running water and dry bark. It was familiar and exciting; I was sort of drifting you see.

The walls were panelled with dark wood. The carpets were a deep rich red.

An ornate banister.

We went into the kitchen.

It was warm and comfortable.

But there was something about it.

Took me a while to figure out what it was.

There was no food.

William put a bottle of Glenfiddich on the table and I took a good lash of it. He sat with me while I drank.

We didn't say anything.

It was quite dark, but I could see his eyes, bright, like a cat.

He seemed to be a bit embarrassed by it and he looked away.

I wanted to believe I was still dreaming.

I wanted to be afraid.

And then he said, 'Six of us live here. The others are women. We need someone like you. It's better if we don't go out. We prefer it if people come here to socialise. Nobody dies, we only take what we need, and they don't become like us. We have always been like this.'

You can go to bars or clubs or wherever. Bring young people. There's a party here every night and you'll find they want to come with you. They leave unharmed and they never remember being here.'

'Can you only come out at night?' I said. He smiled and said it was more convenient for them to live at night, because people are more willing to have a nice time then. 'Is it a nice time?' I said.

He looked at me, his eyes pale, pale blue. 'It's a wonderful time,' he said.

And I believed him.

I was drunk. I was . . .

'Will you do it for me?' he said.

And I felt that saying no was like refusing a friend their dying wish. 'Of course I will,' I said.

And then I was very tired.

He brought me up the dark staircase to a door with more stairs and up into the attic. It was a low ceiling, a bed, a desk, a small window, a bathroom.

'You might like this,' he said.

I turned and saw him standing at a bookcase. Everything I'd need.

I touched them. And I saw a bible. 'You don't mind this book?' I said.

He shook his head.

'Nature made us both,' he said, 'And I don't like garlic because it makes my breath smell. That's the only reason.'

'Superstition,' he said.

Then he frowned and sat on the bed.

'I'll tell you something strange, though,' he said.

'There's a tradition in eastern Europe. You can keep a vampire away from your house by sprinkling rice on your windowsill. The vampire is compelled to count every grain, and luckily he'll still be counting when the morning comes. And for some reason that's sort of true.'

I wasn't sure whether he was joking with me but he seemed to be serious.

He told me he had an overwhelming desire to know how many grains were in a pile. And he seemed to think there was something noble about that. Something that proved he had a deep sense of enquiry and not just a stupid obsession. Fucking rice . . .

That was the first sign I got of his vanity.

That he thought he was more than he was. He turned all his faults into virtues. But that night I was stupid enough and happy enough just to feel . . . ah!

He shook my hand and left the room. I sat at the desk and looked out at the tops of the trees.

And I found myself trying to miss my family. But something wouldn't let me.

I could only miss what they were like years ago.

And that's the way life is, you can't have that, can you?

You can't light a stranger's face with the mention of Santa.

You can only do that to certain people for a certain time.

And then nature makes everybody a cunt because one day you look around and you're all in each other's way.

Mm. There's always going to be a smugness about you listening to this.

As we all take part in this convention. And you will say, 'These vampires are not very believable, are they?'

And you are entitled.

This convention. These restrictions, these rules, they give us that freedom.

I have the freedom to tell you this unhindered, while you can sit there assured that no one is going to get hurt. Possibly offended, but you'll live. We're all quite safe here. Safe to say things like, 'If they were vampires, why don't their victims become vampires?' And you are, of course, relying on the lazy notions foisted upon you by others in the effort to make you buy more popcorn.

But when you find out that they are real, that all changes, you see.

Let's think about it, will we? For a moment. If a vampire bites you and you in turn become a vampire, that's a rule.

A causal, mechanical rule: 'Vampirism is deadly contagious.'

A rule that says their species, like ours, must survive. And that's natural, we suppose. And, that seems to make sense, fine. But we want it both ways.

We want the vampire's bite to be 'magic'. Death-defying, supernatural.

Why?

Why do we need it to be magic?

Because magic doesn't exist?

We don't have to be afraid of what doesn't exist.

Or is it because we envy them?

We're jealous of their power to instil fear in others.

And we can't have that, and if we can't, nothing can?

But we never seem to think for a moment that nature is magic.

We view nature scientifically. We can predict its laws.

But our pride in doing this blinds us. Blinds us to this simple fact: We don't know why there are laws at all.

We may know that the earth goes around the sun. And we may know that this is due to 'gravity'.

But not one of us knows why there is gravity. So don't sit there and cast judgement on the credibility of what I say, when you don't even know why you aren't floating off your seats.

I woke at the desk.

It was morning.

I could half remember hearing laughter during the night. Women.

It was another glorious day.

I had a wash and I went down.

The house was nowhere near as spooky in the bright. It was just dusty.

There was a note on the fridge. 'This is for you.' It was packed with food. There was food all over the place.

I went out the back. Sweet smell, rotten fruit.

I could just see the roofs of the houses on either side.

Just see them above the trees.

They needed repair.

And I knew no one lived there.

There were empty bottles all over the lawn and flies buzzed around the remains on the barbecue.

The sun was too much. I needed to be inside.

My wants were becoming very short term.

You see this was all part of it.

I spent the day reading up at my desk.

Drinking. A life of patronage. That's what I saw myself embarking upon.

Comfortable. I know.

Well.

I only noticed it was dusk when I heard movement downstairs.

Suddenly it was very cold.

There was a woman in the room.

She was black and her hair was dead straight.

She was sleek. Muscular.

I felt like I was floating backwards. That's the effect.

My spine melted into my belly and bubbled away there.

She held a bag out towards me.

I reached for it and she lightly scraped her nails over the back of my hand. And I was a baby wrapped up for the night. And then she was gone.

I sat there with my eyes half closed. Waves of well-being rolling through me. The bag full of clothes. They were just the thing. Dashing. Dishevelled and dashing. They were me.

I could hear more activity.

Doors banging. A row. Someone laughing.

And then footsteps on the stairs.

William.

'Good evening,' he said. 'You look good in that.' Then he sat on the bed and said, 'Mmm, days of cloistered reflection. Reading. Thinking. Are you ready to go?'

'Those women,' I said.

'They won't bother you,' he said, 'They've been warned. Most beautiful women you'll ever see. But fall under their care, you'll wish you were dead, believe me.'

Then he said I should get going.

'I don't know if I'm the social type,' I said. He grinned at me.

'I think you'll find you are,' he said.

He put some money on the desk and then he left.

I stood there, the light fading.

It was time to go. And . . . I suddenly felt . . . light on my feet. Energetic. I wanted to go out.

I went down. I didn't see anyone but it was like I could feel the anticipation. The house. The house had it.

Out on the road I was wondering which way to go, and a taxi just pulled up without me hailing it. I could feel that things were different. I was in it.

I was weak.

'Take me into town,' I said.

That first night I did it.

I walked down into Leicester Square. The tourists and the ticket touts. How the living fuck I was going to invite anyone back to a party was quite fucking beyond me. As was why I was doing this. But Christ knows we all like to be busy. And. It's easy, when you're told what to do. When the choices narrow. When you're under authority. That's why there's so many madcap schemes and bad artists.

And why journalists wank so much, ah?

There's no excuse.

I went into a pub.

Everybody was standing.

I had a drink. I was looking around.

People finished work. Young people, with that shine off them.

This was ridiculous.

But then, suddenly, it wasn't the slightest bit ridiculous.

A young woman was at my elbow trying to get a round.

She was a blondy little thing with a pixie face.

'Excuse me,' I said, and I moved sideways to let her get to the bar.

'Thanks,' she said, 'What'll you have? It's my birthday.'

And I knew. I knew I'd been filled with charm. I'd been made attractive.

This was the gift I'd been given to bring people back.

'Your birthday!' I said, 'Please, allow me.'

'No,' she said, 'I couldn't, I'm with a group.'

I looked around. They were perfect.

Twenties. Good looking. Lots of energy. 'I'll have a pint, then,' I said.

Her name was Dominique.

She worked for a magazine.

The people she was with were college friends. From Oxford.

She invited me to join them. Which I duly did.

And duly got bolloxed out of my fucking face. And held them enthralled with my brutal wit. We looked like a bunch of saps and their rich daddy, I think. We were a tidy half dozen. At closing time we went for a pizza and wine, and more wine.

The stupid evening ablaze with drink and bullshit.

And then I had an 'idea'.

'Let's all go back to my house, for God's sake!' And I have to admit it. I was curious. I didn't like them. I was looking forward to seeing what was going to happen to them. I think you'd call that, having a streak in you.

And naturally by this time, we're inseparable and we pile into taxis.

All dry wit and our best clothes.

Chugging through the lights into the suburbs.

Down the dark road to William's house.

Music was drifting around from the back garden.

I led them down the side passage.

And I shut the gate.

There were candles lit all around the garden.

But there was no one there.

Tables were laid with drink.

We sat on stone benches.

I slugged on a bottle of wine.

But it was more than just being drunk in that place. It was like drowning. Gulping water for air and not being able to stop.

The youngsters fell around, dancing. In each others' arms.

And then, gradually, I noticed that there were more people. Moving among them.

The women. Jesus Christ. Heart-breakingly beautiful women.

You could see them and you couldn't.

Just like beauty in real life.

Sometimes it's there, and sometimes it should be. And it's not.

And after a while, I could feel the air. It began to fizz with pointless regret. And slowly, in twos and threes, they began to lie down in the grass.

And the moon and stars were shining down on this, and it was just another one of the things that goes on.

Nothing special.

I went to bed.

I woke up about ten.

Only the faintest twinge of a hangover. I'd gotten off lightly.

I went downstairs for some water, and there at the kitchen table, slumped over was Dominique.

I woke her. She was weak and she had a headache but that was all. I mean, fuck, I gave her some paracetamol, you know? I mean . . .

She couldn't remember anything about the party.

We went around waking her friends.

They were all over the place, on the floor, on the grass, one was even in a fucking hedge. I got them up.

Dominique gave me a kiss. I grabbed her hand. And they were happy, you know? They talked about getting a cure.

I saw them out. No harm done. I tidied up a bit. It was okay. Doing this. Being this thing.

I did it again the next night, and the one after. And after that. And that's how the next while was.

Flirting in bars. Getting . . . affection.

Back for a party. Getting them out in the morning. Everyone happy to be there and happy to leave.

Every time I did it, it was going to be the last time, but . . .

I'd think about the reception I'd get back in Dublin, and I wasn't up to it. I'd give it a few more days.

And . . . I'd keep giving it a few more days. I stayed away from the vampires, as much as I could.

The only one I spoke to was William. But I'd wish he'd leave me alone.

I'd be in the attic, and I'd read, and . . . I even began to do a little bit of writing. It was coming a bit easier, you see, because there were no knackers like me around the place who were going to tear it apart. It was just small things, things I'd remember. But I'll be straight with you. It wasn't very good.

And I'd be doing this you see and William would come to visit me.

I didn't want him to.

There was something.

He looked like us. But. He wasn't a human. And I had to think to work out what made him different.

And it was hard to think in that place. But I made the effort and I worked it out. How he was different from us. And it showed me what we are. What it is that makes us what we are.

But it took a good while.

I was curious about them of course. I began to have a look at them, sleeping. Sometimes they were all in the one bed. And sometimes I couldn't find them.

But they slept just like us.

And they'd wake up if I made a noise. Once, one of the women opened her eyes and I immediately got weak.

Weak in here. Took everything just to get back to my room.

And I had to lie down.

I stopped checking on them.

There was a gap.

And so, there I'd be, trying to write something. Trying to capture the care I once had, you see. My kids on Christmas eve. Something like that.

And I'd feel him come in.

And of all things, he'd talk about art. And advise me about writing.

It was always the same.

The art object is different from every other object, he said, because it's not for anything.

A chair only is what it is because it's for sitting on. A knife only is what it is because it's for cutting.

But art is for itself.

Just as goodness is. It's for it's own sake. Art is like having a go at making virtue. And he'd criticise me for my fear.

Fear of my work not being 'good' enough. The act itself is good, he said. You see how cerebral he was, nothing else. And I could never stand a pep talk. All that glib psychoanalytic wank.

So one day I got annoyed and said it must be brilliant living for so long, gathering all this wisdom.

He didn't say anything for a while. He looked a bit shook. And then in his true, corny, way. He told me a story.

A, Jesus, a fucking, story.

He told me there was a man where he came from, a long time ago.

And he was a woodsman.

And he was one of the happiest men who ever lived. Because he had married a woman who he loved more than himself.

His heart swelled at the thought of her. She was present to him at every moment of his lonely day out in the woods.

His only disappointment in life was that they couldn't have children.

Their innocence.

But it wasn't to be and he accepted his lot.

And that's what this man's life was like. And one day he was working out in the woods. And he heard someone crying. It was a strange sound. Near and far away at the same time. He dropped his axe and he went towards it. He called out and he was guided by the cries. And he saw why the sound was so strange. In the woods was a well and the crying came from the well.

He looked down, and in the water far below was an old man desperately clinging to the bucket, trying to stay afloat.

So the woodsman worked and strained and pulled him out. And then lay him down to recover. But it was too late. The old man was dying.

With his last breaths, he thanked the woodsman for his kindness and told him to look in his satchel. And in the satchel were tools for watchmaking. And there was a new watch. The most beautiful watch the woodsman had ever seen.

The old man told the woodsman that he wanted him to keep it.

It could tell more than just the time he said. And then he died.

And it wasn't until many years later that the woodsman found out what the watch's secret was. He was out in the woods one winter's day and it was getting dark.

He looked at the watch but it had stopped.

He tried winding it but it didn't seem to work. But then he wound it backwards and something changed.

The light. Somehow it had become brighter. The sun was higher in the sky.

He wound it back another hour and the sun rose higher.

He could travel in time.

He wound it forward again and the sun went down.

Understandably he was a bit fucking amazed.

You see, this is the art of understatement. And he never told anyone about it, not even his beloved wife.

It was a secret.

And being an honest fellow, he never saw what practical use such a thing could have. He never used it to travel.

He wasn't interested. Everything he loved was in the present.

That was, until his wife died.

And the woodsman was heartbroken.

And naturally he couldn't resist going back a little, now and then, to hold her once again. And his infatuation never ceased.

He was fascinated by her.

He was in love, do you see?

And he began to go back a little further. Until it got to the stage where he went back further than he'd ever gone.

To see her as a child, before he had known her.

He was an old man watching this child play.

But this only made him feel his loss even more. He knew his time with her was over.

He faced up to it and decided he must live alone until he saw her again in heaven.

But he found that the watch was now truly broken and would not wind at all.

He was stuck in the past.

Where nobody knew him. Not even his wife, since she was just a little girl.

But she was all he had. He panicked.

Terror. He took the child.

He picked her up and ran into the woods with her in his frail arms.

And she was crying and screaming.

And he couldn't let her go.

And then he was tired and he couldn't go any further. And they fell together in the leaves. And he held on to her. You know?

And the townspeople caught him and beat him.

And left him.

When William finished telling me this we were . . . very quiet.

And then I asked him, what does it mean? And he didn't know.

He looked a bit bewildered. And then he laughed and fucked off.

He didn't know what his story meant.

He knew he was supposed to be informed by it but it was just a story that he told.

A story about not being able to get back.

And that was all.

And that's what makes us different.

We reflect.

They don't.

They see what they want. They get it.

Do anything to get it.

William couldn't hold a child any more than, than you or I could push a glass of water away when we're parched.

And I think he wanted . . .

That was the horror of the whole thing.

The cunt wanted a conscience.

He fucking regretted not being able to regret the things he did.

And when I realised this, he began to disgust me.

Clinging to all this human bollocks, lecturing me on what was wrong with my life.

This unreflective animal. Christ.

All his foibles. His virtues. For fuck's sake. Man was a butcher. Slept all day.

Came out and bit people. Fucking knacker.

So it came to . . .

We were in the kitchen one evening before I went out for some youngsters.

And to be honest with you, as usual, I was a bit pissed.

There we were, leaning on the worktop, all philosophical. All ordinary.

How the world had fucked me up and this was where I belonged.

Where there were no great expectations of me. Where I could relax.

You know? Like he knew anything beyond how hungry he felt.

And this, the immorality of what I'd been doing over the last few years.

Jesus, I knew that!

If I didn't I wouldn't have had a problem.

I knew what I'd been doing was wrong.

That's why I did it.

I enjoyed the looks of fear and hatred I'd gotten whenever I went into an actors' pub.

I behaved that way, because it was wrong. But William had no because.

He couldn't buck nature.

He had no choice the way a dog has no choice.

Reasons don't come into it.

And there he was talking to me about the autonomy of the art object and things like this.

It was sad. It was boring.

And these vampire bitches moving through the house. Brushing by.

These . . . things men would die for.

Getting in here. Bringing every whim you've got firmly down into your pants.

I can't overstate their power to distract.

I was all confused whenever they came near me.

And William knew this. You know?

He'd let them be around, so I couldn't think straight.

So he could have the floor.

Fuck. He was welcome to it.

I had nothing to say to him.

I just thought, 'Ah, Jesus, would you just . . . '

You know?

And I grabbed this jar of rice and I smashed it on the floor.

William was a bit startled at first, but then, suddenly, I was just another object in the room. And him, and I think two others . . . got down on the floor and started to count. I thought I better get going.

William was saying, 'Wait, come, come back.'

But he was lost in the rice.

And I had a moment of clarity.

No more messing . . .

This was the last night I was doing this. This was the last batch of idiots I was bringing back.

And after that . . . Well I didn't know. I'd see.

I took a cab into Soho.

A bar with a late licence.

I sat there for a few hours and it began to fill up as all the other bars closed.

It was a kip, and I had to be the oldest codger in the place.

But the old charm was there and pretty soon I was getting greeted. And smiled at. Who did they think I was, for fuck's sake? And I was at the bar with this group of rich kids.

Exchanging stories about the old days that are all gone now.

'Oh yeah, I knew them all. Name them. I knew them. He was a drinker. Let me tell you. Let me tell you.' Mmm.

'What are we doing here? I know somewhere we can go.' Yeah.

I think I was aware of her before I saw her.

The first thing I saw was her feet.

Bare feet in open sandals.

The sinews in her ankle shifting with her weight.

Helen.

She was looking at me.

These people were actors.

She had every right to stare at me.

What I'd done.

And as far as anyone knew, from Dublin, I had disappeared.

And here I was regaling the young things in London.

I looked her in the eye.

I could feel the tears coming.

Made me annoyed.

I was embarrassed.

I wanted to kill everybody. Get out.

But I'd forgotten the charm, hadn't 1?

She leaned forward and kissed me.

I could have anything I wanted.

'People have been wondering about you,' she said.

'People . . . Let me get you a drink,' I said. And I bought a round.

You see this was the first time I'd been surrounded by artists and actually felt in charge.

This was the ideal last batch.

In the morning, none of them would remember what had happened.

And I would know.

And they'd be fools in my eyes forever. I had power now.

But Helen.

This could be different in her case. In our case.

I could keep her away from the others.

Bring her up to the attic. Lock the door.

And she'd be . . .

She'd want to lie down with me.

Until it got bright.

And a big clock would go back, and when we woke up, how the world would have changed. That was my wish.

'Let's go,' I said.

'Come on,' and we piled into cabs. And for the second time in as many months she was beside me.

Her cool body.

A soothing fucking you know? A . . .

And all the others were drunk as maniacs.

I leaned into her.

'You've got to stay beside me tonight,' I said. She didn't even question it. I was beginning to miss things.

The spell was breaking.

Human company.

We got to the house.

Probably the most people I'd ever brought back.

I held her hand.

And I led everybody around the back.

And I got a shock.

The vampires were there already.

All around the garden.

Quiet. Watching us. No music tonight. The young actors didn't care.

They were caught up in the easy confusion of the place. Ten times as drunk as when they'd left the bar.

And the worst thing.

William was only looking at me.

He was annoyed at me.

I'd let him down.

He'd been all clever one minute and the next he was down on the floor counting rice.

I'd reminded him what he was and what he wasn't.

The women didn't waste any time.

Already there were tangles of limbs.

And William was just looking at me.

I took Helen into the house.

She was nodding off.

I had to get her out.

I began to panic.

As much as one can panic when every thought is like looking for something in . . . tar. We went into the hall.

And one of the women was on the stairs.

I couldn't move.

I couldn't feel Helen.

She was gone.

The woman came towards me.

I was in for it.

My legs began to wobble.

She took me in her arms and lifted me. Dancing slowly in the hall.

We were up the banister, we were down in a corner. We were drifting.

The joy of submitting to something like that.

To put yourself in someone's care.

Trust has nothing to do with it.

It's abandon.

And then the stupid cow bit me.

And it fucking hurt.

My arm was getting cold.

I passed out.

And then, thump, we were on the ground. I could feel my weight again.

I was a fat bastard on the floor.

The woman was on top of me.

She was dozy.

There was blood all down my shirt. Down my pants.

Only consolation I had was she might get a hangover that'd knock her off her feet for days. She'd bitten the wrong fellow. It would have been nice to lie there for a while. But the alarm bells were ringing. I had to find Helen.

Fuck. I couldn't believe I'd been bitten. I went back out to the garden.

Dawn was coming. The vampires were gone in. People lay about.

Helen wasn't there.

She wasn't in the kitchen or the lounge. She wasn't on the stairs.

Then I heard talking.

It was in the attic.

It was William.

His singsong.

His lilt.

I crept up. Slowly.

He was talking about me.

About the world and how it had spoiled me.

Ah, he was spoofing.

Pretending he could think.

I got to the door.

Helen was on my bed.

She had hardly any clothes on.

She'd been bitten too.

And William was sitting beside her.

Talking rubbish.

The epitome of nature's thoughtlessness.

The desire to survive.

That's all he was.

But he didn't know that.

And looking at the two of them there. No comparison.

She was so beautiful.

And he was a black looking thing that was hardly even there.

And I was more her than him. A good feeling.

And I just said, 'Leave her alone you smelly prick.'

He looked up at me, and I swear to God, his eyes were blazing red. I'm not joking. But, because of that, the situation didn't seem very real. And I wasn't scared. 'Helen,' I said, 'Get up.'

She obeyed me the way a sick child does.

Slowly, with resignation.

'Do you want me to leave?' he said. 'No, stay there,' I said, 'I'm going.'

He looked at the bookcase for a moment, and then he said, 'You won't be happy.'

'Probably not,' I said, 'But it wouldn't be much fun if I was.' Know what I mean?

Then I put my arm around Helen and brought her down the stairs.

He didn't follow us and I don't why he let me go.

Maybe wanting a conscience is the same as having one.

Because it's all the same effort, isn't it? Maybe he was just imitating us.

I lay Helen on a couch with one of her pals. She slept. I gave her a kiss, and then I left them to their hangovers.

The summer was fading.

There was a chill in the morning.

I walked down the street and I thought about the fuss people were going to make of me.

The potential it gave me to bully sympathy out of everybody.

Back from my breakdown.

On the right track again, yeah?

I'd 'Embrace My Second Chance.'

I'd do a piece about 'Getting Back.'

Getting back in touch with things.

Talking To My Wife.

Giving My Children My Advice.

I had my health.

I had resolve.

But most important.

Over everything else.

I had a story.

So, were they real?
Or were they a dream?
Well, I've got to ask you, what the hell
isn't a dream?
Your projections for the future. Your fantasies.
Your fears. Your rude awakenings.
What the hell is that if it's not any night's sleep?
And that person you fell head over heels for.
What the hell was that,
What was the moment it hit you?,
Love, Christ. If it was love at first sight,
what the hell you doing giving some stranger
the benefit of the doubt? Entrusting them
with everything you've got?
Because of what you wanted them to be?
Well, that's a dream-life if ever there was one,
And if it wasn't love at first sight, and
it was a gradual thing. Like a wound healing.
Let me ask you this: don't you begin to resent
that person in equal amounts? For sneaking
up on you, and denying you all the chaotic
excitement you felt your love should have been?
And if neither of these are true for you and
you're in the middle of it, and you haven't
fucking blown it yet. And you're the happiest
person in the room . . .
Well, your presence blesses everyone else here,
doesn't it? Because you're the embodiment of hope,
aren't you? You're hope incarnate.
Where are you? Where are you?
Where?

THE WEIR

For Michael, Clare, Karen and Margaret
And for Gina

Characters

JACK, *fifties.*
BRENDAN, *thirties.*
JIM, *forties.*
FINBAR, *late forties.*
VALERIE, *thirties.*

The play is set in a rural part of Ireland, Northwest Leitrim or Sligo. Present day. Stage Setting: a small rural bar.

The Weir is a Royal Court Theatre commissioned play

A counter; left with three bar taps. The spirits are not mounted, simply left on the shelf. There are three stools at the counter.

There is a fireplace, right. Near this is a low table with some small stools and a bigger, more comfortable chair, nearest the fire. There is another small table, front, with a stool or two.

On the wall, back, are some old black and white photographs, A ruined Abbey. People posing near a newly erected ESB weir. A town in a cove with mountains around it.

An old television is mounted up in a corner, right. There is a small radio on a shelf behind the bar.

A door, right, is the main entrance to the bar. A door, back, leads to the toilets and a yard.

This bar is part of a house and the house is part of a farm.

The door, right, opens. JACK comes in. He wears a suit which looks a bit big for him, and a white shirt open at the collar. Over this is a dirty anorak. He takes the anorak off and hangs it up. He wipes his boots aggressively on a mat.

He goes behind the counter. He selects a glass and pours himself a pint of stout. He puts it on the bar and turns to the till, which he opens with practised, if uncertain, ease. He puts the money in and takes the change.

As he does this, the door at back opens. BRENDAN comes in. He wears a sweater, heavy cord pants and a pair of slip-on shoes. He carries a bucket with peat briquettes. He goes to the fire, barely acknowledging JACK, just his voice.

BRENDAN. Jack.

JACK. Brendan.

BRENDAN (*tending the fire*). That's some wind.

JACK (*topping up his pint*). It is.

BRENDAN. Must have been against you, was it?

> JACK *comes out from behind the counter and stands looking at the fire.*

JACK. It was. It was against me till I came around the Knock. It was a bit of shelter then.

BRENDAN *also stands looking at the fire.*

BRENDAN. Yeah it's a funny one. It's coming from the north.

JACK. Mm. Ah, it's mild enough though.

BRENDAN. Ah yeah. It's balmy enough. (*Pause.*) It's balmy enough.

BRENDAN *goes in behind the counter.*

JACK. Were you in Carrick today?

BRENDAN. I wasn't, no. I had the sisters over doing their rounds. Checking up on me.

JACK. Checking their investments.

BRENDAN. Oh yeah. Course, they don't have a fucking clue what they're looking for, d'you know? They're just vaguely . . . you know.

JACK. Keeping the pressure on you.

BRENDAN. This is it. (*Pause.*) At me to sell the top field.

JACK. You don't use it much.

BRENDAN. No. No I don't. Too much trouble. Driving a herd up. But I know they're looking at it, all they see is new cars for their hubbies, you know?

JACK. Mm. You're not just trying to spite them? Get them vexed? Hah?

BRENDAN. Not at all. I'm, just. It's a grand spot up there. Ah, I don't know. Just . . . (*Short pause.*)

JACK. They over the whole day?

BRENDAN. They got here about two. They'd gone for lunch in the Arms. Got their story straight. Ah they were gone and all about half four.

JACK. They've no attachment to the place, no?

BRENDAN. No they don't. They look around, and it's . . . 'Ah yeah . . . ' you know? (*They laugh a little.*)

BRENDAN. It's gas.

JACK. Mm.

BRENDAN. Were you in Carrick yourself?

JACK. I was. I flew in about eleven, threw on a fast bet. Jimmy was there, we went for a quick one in the Pot.

BRENDAN. How's Jimmy? And the ma?

JACK. Ah. Jimmy. Be in tonight. He put me on to a nice one. We got her at eleven to four.

BRENDAN. You're learning to listen, hah?

JACK. Ah. Fuck that sure. I know, but I've been having the worst run of shit, you wouldn't believe. I was that desperate, I'd listen to anybody.

BRENDAN. Go on out of that.

JACK. Ah no. No no. Fair dues. I'll say it. He got us a right one. And it's good, you know. Break a streak like that.

BRENDAN. You're a user.

JACK (laughs). There's worse.

BRENDAN. Yeah. There might be.

JACK. But, ah, he was telling me. Did you know about Maura Nealon's house?

BRENDAN. No.

JACK. Well. Jim says he met Finbar Mack down in the Spar. Finally, either sold or's renting the, the thing, after how many years it's sat there?

BRENDAN. Jays, four or five in anyway.

JACK. Jim says five this month. And Finbar's going bananas with the great fella that he is. Patting himself on the back, goodo, and talking about the new resident. Who, he says, is a fine girl. Single. Down from Dublin and all this. And Finbar's nearly leaving the wife just to have a chance with this one. Only messing, like. But he's going to bring her in here tonight. This is the nearest place to old Maura's. Bring her in for a drink, introduce her to the natives.

BRENDAN. The dirty bastard. I don't want him using in here for that sort of carry on. A married man like him.

JACK. Ah he's only old shit. He wouldn't have the nerve. Sure, how far'd he get anyway? The fucking head on him. He's only having a little thrill. Bringing her around. And I'll tell you what it is as well. He's coming in here with her. And he's the one. He's the one that's 'with' her, in whatever fucking . . . sense

we're talking about. He's bringing her in. And there's you and
me, and the Jimmy fella, the muggins's, the single fellas. And
he's the married fella. And he's going 'Look at this! There's
obviously something the fuck wrong with yous. Yous are single
and you couldn't get a woman near this place. And look at me.
I'm hitched. I'm over and done with, and I'm having to beat
them off.'

BRENDAN. Yeah. That's the way cunts always go about their
business. It's intrusive, it's bad manners, it's . . .

JACK. Ah, it's a juvenile carry on. You know?

BRENDAN. Mm.

JACK. Let her come in herself.

BRENDAN. Yeah. That'd be better. That'd make more sense, for
fuck's sake.

JACK. Leave her be . . . (*Short pause.*) Don't know if I'll stay
actually.

BRENDAN. Mm.

Pause. JACK drains his pint and brings his glass to the bar.

JACK. Go on.

BRENDAN takes the glass and pours a fresh pint.

JACK. Don't want to leave Jimmy in the lurch. You know? Trying
to hold his own in the Finbar Mack world of big business.

They laugh a little.

BRENDAN. Fucking . . . Jimmy talking all that crack with Finbar.

JACK. But that's the thing though. The Jimmy fella's got more
going on up here (*Head.*) than popular opinion would give him
credit for.

BRENDAN. Sure, don't we know too well, for God's sake?

JACK. I know.

BRENDAN. We know only too well.

JACK counts change out on the bar.

JACK. Would you give us ten Silk Cut please, Brendan?

BRENDAN. Red?

JACK. Please.

*BRENDAN hands over the cigarettes and finishes pulling the
pint.*

JACK. Good man.

BRENDAN counts the money off the bar. JACK pauses before drinking.

JACK. Are we right?

BRENDAN. Close enough. Cheers.

JACK. Good luck.

JACK takes a long drink. Pause.

JACK. I know I do be at you. I'll keep at you though.

BRENDAN. About what?

JACK. Don't be messing. Come on.

BRENDAN. Ah.

JACK. A young fella like you. And this place a right going concern.

BRENDAN. Ah. The odd time. You know, the odd time I'd think about it.

JACK. You should though.

BRENDAN. Well then, so should you.

JACK. Would you go on? An auld fella like me!

BRENDAN. Would you listen to him?

JACK. Ah, sure what would I want with giving up my freedom?

BRENDAN. Well then me as well!

Pause.

JACK. Tch. Maybe. Maybe there's something to be said for the old independence.

BRENDAN. Ah there is.

Pause.

JACK. A lot to be said for it.

BRENDAN. Mm. (*Pause.*) Mm.

JACK. Cheers!

BRENDAN. Good luck.

JACK takes a long drink. The main door opens and JIMMY enters. He takes off an anorak to reveal a festive looking cardigan. JACK pretends not to notice him.

JACK (*winks*). Oh yes, Brendan, the luck is changing. I got me and the Jimmy fella onto a nice one today. That fella would want to listen to me a little more often, I tell you.

JIM. I'm going to have to start charging you for tips, am I?

JACK. Ah James! What'll you have?

JIM. Teach you some manners. Teach him some manners Brendan, ha? Small one please Jack.

BRENDAN. Small one.

JACK. Sure it'd take more than money to put manners on me, ha? Brendan.

BRENDAN. It'd take a bomb under you.

JACK. Now you said it. Bomb is right. That wind still up, Jim?

JIM. Oh it is, yeah. Warm enough though.

JACK. We were just saying.

BRENDAN. For a Northerly.

JIM. Oh that's from the west now.

BRENDAN. Is it?

JIM. Oh yeah that's a Westerly.

JACK. Must've shifted.

JIM. Mm.

Pause. JIM comes to the bar.

JIM. Thanking you.

JACK. Good luck.

JIM. Good luck.

BRENDAN. Good luck.

JACK counts change out on the bar.

JACK. Are we right?

BRENDAN counts and pushes a coin back towards JACK.

BRENDAN (*taking rest*). Now we are. Sure it's hard enough to come by without giving it away.

JACK. This is it. Oh. (*To* JIM.) Are you doing anything tomorrow?

JIM. What time?

JACK. I have to get out to Conor Boland. His tractor is packed up. And I have Father Donal's jalopy in since Tuesday. Said I'd change the oil. Haven't done it yet. Would you come in and do it so I can go over to Boland's?

JIM. It'd have to be early. I'm dropping the mother out to Sligo.

JACK. Well, whatever. Is that all right?

JIM. Ah, it should be yeah. Pint?

JACK. Not for the moment. You go on.

JIM. Pint please Brendan.

BRENDAN. How's the mammy today?

JIM. Ah you know?

JACK. Tch. I have to get down and see her. I keep saying it.

JIM. Well whenever, whenever you want.

BRENDAN. Do you think you'll do anything?

JIM. About?

BRENDAN. About up there on your own and all that?

JIM. Ah. Sure where would I go? And I was talking to Finbar Mack. Be lucky to get twenty thousand for the place. Sure where would you be going with that? (*Short pause.*) You know!

JACK. With the acre?

JIM. Ah yeah, the whole . . . the whole thing.

JACK. Ah you're grand with the few little jobs around here.

JIM. Ah.

JACK. You'll be cosy enough.

Pause.

BRENDAN. Jack was telling me about Finbar. And the new eh . . .

JIM. Mmm, yeah, I was telling him earlier.

JACK. I was telling him.

JIM. I've seen her since.

BRENDAN. Oh yeah?

JIM. Yeah, they were in Finbar's car going up the Head.

JACK *and* BRENDAN *exchange a look.*

BRENDAN. Fucking hell.

JACK. Like a courting couple or something.

JIM. He's showing her the area.

JACK. Jesus. 'The area.' He's a terrible fucking thick.

JIM. Ah, he has them all jabbering down in Carrick.

JACK. Yeah. I wish he wasn't bringing her in here. You know?

BRENDAN. Sure he hasn't been in here since Freddie Mack drowned.

JACK. What the fuck, is he doing? You know?

JIM. Ah. She's new. This is the only place near to her.

JACK. She can . . . (*Nodding.*) find her own way surely, Jim, come on.

BRENDAN. Well it's, you know. If it's courtesy, which is one thing and a business . . . act or whatever, you know, you have to say, well . . . you know, okay. But if it's all messy, I'm trapped in here behind this fucking thing. And you wish he'd stop acting the mess. I have to respect whatever, they're . . .

JACK. Well this is it, we're here.

JIM. It's probably not really anything.

Short pause.

JACK. What age would she be, about, Jim?

JIM. Em, I only saw her for a sec. I'd say, (*Beat.*) like they were in the car and all, I'd say about thirties. Very nice looking.

Pause.

JACK. Dublin woman.

JIM. Dublin.

Short pause.

BRENDAN. She's no one in the area, no?

JIM. No she's . . . coming down, you know?

JACK. Mm. (*Pause.*) Yeah.

JIM. Good luck. (*Drinks.*)

JACK. Cheers. (*Drinks.*)

BRENDAN. Good luck, boys.

JACK. Another week or two now, You'll be seeing the first of the Germans.

BRENDAN. Mm. Stretch in the evening, yeah.

JACK. You wouldn't ever think of clearing one of the fields for a few caravans.

BRENDAN. Ah.

JACK. The top field.

BRENDAN. Ah there wouldn't be a lot of shelter up there. There'd be a wind up there that'd cut you.

JIM. D'you know what you could do? The herd'd be grand up there, and you could, you know, down here.

BRENDAN. Ah. (*Short pause.*) They do be around anyway. You know yourself.

JIM. Ah, they do.

JACK. You're not chasing the extra revenue.

BRENDAN. Or the work!

JIM. They do be around right enough.

BRENDAN. I'll leave the campsites to Finbar, ha? He'll sort them out.

JACK. Ah, Finbar's in need of the few shekels.

They laugh.

BRENDAN. Ah, he's in dire need of the few bob, the poor fella, that's right, that's right.

JACK. Mm.

Pause.

BRENDAN. Yeah. If you had all the . . . families out there. On their holliers. And all the kids and all. You'd feel the evenings turning. When they'd be leaving. And whatever about how quiet it is now. It'd be fucking shocking quiet then. (*Short pause.*) You know?

Pause.

JACK. Mm.

JIM. D'you want a small one, Jack?

JACK. Go on.

JIM. Two small ones please Brendan.

BRENDAN. The small fellas.

BRENDAN *works.*

JACK. Are you having one yourself?

BRENDAN. I'm debating whether to have one.

JACK. Ah have one, and don't be acting the mess.

BRENDAN. Go on then.

He pours himself a glass of whiskey.

JACK. Good man. (*Short pause.*) A few shekels, ha? (*They smile.*) Mm.

JACK *takes out his cigarettes.*

JACK. Jim?

JIM. Oh cheers Jack.

JIM *takes one.*

JACK. Brendan?

BRENDAN. Fags and all, ha?

JACK. Go on, they're good for you.

BRENDAN. (*Taking one.*) Go on.

They light up from a match which JACK strikes. They puff contentedly for a moment.

JIM (*lifting glass*). Keep the chill out.

JACK. This is it. Cheers.

BRENDAN. Cheers men.

JIM. Good luck.

They drink.

JACK. Now.

JIM. D'yous hear a car?

Pause.

BRENDAN. No.

JIM. That's Finbar's car.

Pause.

JIM. He's parked.

JACK. I didn't see the lights.

JIM. He came around the Knock.

From off, they hear FINBAR*'s voice.*

FINBAR (*off*). Ah yeah, sure half the townland used to nearly live in here.

JACK. There we are now.

The door opens and FINBAR *brings* VALERIE *in.*

FINBAR. That's it now.

FINBAR *wears a light cream coloured suit and an open collar.* VALERIE *wears jeans and a sweater.*

FINBAR. Men. This is Valerie. She's just moved into Maura Nealon's old house.

JACK. Hello, how are you?

JACK *shakes her hand.*

VALERIE. Hello.

FINBAR. This is Jack Mullen. He has a little garage up around the Knock.

VALERIE. How are you?

JACK *nods politely.*

JACK. Now.

FINBAR. This is Jim Curran. Does a bit of work with Jack.

VALERIE *and* JIM *shake hands.*

VALERIE. Pleased to meet you.

JIM. Pleased to meet you.

FINBAR. And this is Brendan. Brendan Byrne.

VALERIE. Hello.

They shake hands.

BRENDAN. How are you?

FINBAR. This is his bar. And all the land I showed you. All back down the hill. That's all his farm.

VALERIE. Oh right. It's all lovely here.

BRENDAN. Oh yeah. It's a grand spot all along . . . for going for a walk or that, all down the cliffs.

FINBAR. Oh it's lovely all down here. What'll you have?

BRENDAN. Oh, I'll get this, Finbar. No. What, what do you want?

FINBAR. Oh now, ha ha. Eh, I'll have a pint, then, what? Says you, if it's going, ha?

BRENDAN. Pint. Valerie?

VALERIE. Em. Could I have . . . Do you have . . . em, a glass of white wine?

Pause.

BRENDAN (*going*). Yeah. I'm just going to run in the house.

VALERIE Oh no. Don't. Don't put yourself to any trouble.

BRENDAN. No. No it's no trouble. I have a bottle.

He goes.

FINBAR. He probably has a bottle of the old vino, from feckin . . . Christmas, what?

JACK. It's not too often the . . . the . . . wine does be flowing in here.

VALERIE. I'm all embarrassed now.

FINBAR. Don't be silly. Sit up there now, and don't mind us. Don't mind these country fellas.

JACK. Jays. You're not long out of it yourself, says the man, ha?

FINBAR (*winks*). They're only jealous Valerie because I went to the town to seek my fortune. And they all stayed out here on the bog picking their holes.

JACK. Janey, now ha? You didn't have very hard to seek. Just a quick look in big Finbar's will, I think is more like it.

FINBAR. Big Finbar's will! That's shrewd investment, boy. That's an eye for the gap.

JACK. Yeah, he probably fleeced you on Maura Nealon's house, did he?

VALERIE. I have to say I don't think so.

FINBAR. Good girl.

VALERIE. But it's very reasonable all around here, isn't it?

FINBAR. Oh it is, yeah . You know . . .

Short pause.

JACK. Is there much doing up in it?

FINBAR. Ah, hardly any.

VALERIE. There's one or two floorboards. A bit of paint.

JACK (*indicating* JIM). Well, there's your man. If you're looking for a good pair of hands.

VALERIE. Is that right?

JIM. I'll have a look for you, if you like. I know that house.

FINBAR Don't be charging her through the nose now.

JIM. Ah ha, now.

BRENDAN returns with a bottle of wine.

FINBAR. You'd want to be giving her a neighbourly . . . rate, now, is the thing, ha?

JIM. Oh yeah.

JACK. Would you listen to him? 'Neighbourly rates'. Wasn't by giving neighbourly rates you bought half the fucking town.

FINBAR. Half the town! (*To* VALERIE, *winking.*) I bought the whole town. Eye for the gap, you see.

JACK. Eye for your gap is right.

FINBAR (*To* BRENDAN). How long has that been in there? Lying in some drawer . . .

BRENDAN (*corkscrewing the bottle*). Ah, it was a . . . present or some . . . (*Looks at label.*) 1990. Now. Vintage, ha? (*They laugh.*) I hope it's all right now.

VALERIE. It's grand. I won't know the difference.

They watch BRENDAN open the bottle. He pours a tumbler full and holds it up to the light and sniffs it.

BRENDAN. I think it's all right.

FINBAR. Ah, would you give the woman the feckin thing. The tongue's hanging out of her.

Again they watch as VALERIE takes the glass.

VALERIE. Thanks Brendan.

She drinks.

VALERIE. That's gorgeous. I'm not joking now. That's lovely.

FINBAR. Good.

BRENDAN. I'm putting it in the fridge for you Valerie.

He does.

FINBAR. Good man.

Pause. FINBAR nods at VALERIE, a reassuring 'hello'.

(*To* JACK *and* JIM.) How d'yous do today, boys?

JACK. Are you codding me? With this fella? Eleven to four we got her at, came down to six to four.

FINBAR. Sheer Delight was it?

JACK. Yeah. Kenny down in the shop, the knacker. Adjusting everything how this fella's betting.

JIM (*indicating* JACK). This fella hardly listens to me.

JACK. Ah now.

FINBAR. He's too proud, Jimmy. Too proud to admit when he needs a tip off you.

JACK (*emphatically*). I . . . have . . . my policy on this. And I have my principle. I am the first one to say it about this fella. See, usually, Valerie, usually, not all the time, Jim's not too far off the mark.

FINBAR. 'Too far off the mark!' (*To* VALERIE.) He's bang on the nail!

BRENDAN *places a pint on the bar.*

FINBAR. Thanks Brendan.

He puts his hand in his pocket, BRENDAN *waves him away.*

JACK. Not every time.

FINBAR. Thanks, thanks a million. (*To* VALERIE.) He is.

JACK. Bang on the nail is one thing, from judgement . . . and . . . But, and Jimmy knows I don't mean anything by this, and I know because we've spoken about this before. He has a scientific approach. He studies the form. And, no offence, he has a bit of time to be doing that. He studies it Valerie, and fair play to him, right? Do you bet on horses?

VALERIE. No.

FINBAR. Good girl.

JACK. Well he, how much, Jim, would you make in a month? On the horses.

JIM. Ah it evens out Jack. Like I'm not eh . . . I don't . . .

JACK. How much was it you got that time? When Cheltenham was on that time.

JIM. Two hundred and twenty.

JACK. Two hundred and twenty pounds, Valerie, in like three days, now. Right?

JIM. Yeah but . . .

JACK. Yeah, I know, that'd be a bigger win. But he was planning for Cheltenham for weeks, Valerie, and . . . tinkering with his figures and his . . . you know. He'd be in here with the paper up on the counter there. Brendan? Before Cheltenham?

BRENDAN. Oh yeah.

JACK. Right? Now, but I'm more: 'Ah, sure, I'll have an old bet, like.' Do you know that way? And that's what I do, and to tell you the truth I don't be too bothered. It's a bit of fun and that's what it should be. And so . . . I'm not going to listen to 'Do this and do that, and you'll be right.' Just to get a few bob. There's no fun in that. And the principle of it, you know?

FINBAR. Ah, the principle of the thing is to win a few quid and don't be giving out.

JACK. Who's giving out? I'm not giving out. All I'm just saying is that the way I go at it, the principle's not the science. It's the luck, it's the something that's not the facts and figures of it.

FINBAR. Jaysus. And do you and Kenny get down on your knees and lash a few quick Hail Marys out before he stamps your docket or something?

JACK. Ah it's not like that. I'm not talking about that. For fuck's sake.

FINBAR. Anyway, what the hell are you talking about? You took Jimmy's tip today, and you won, so what the hell are you talking about? (*To others.*) Ha?

JACK. Ah yeah but . . . now listen because . . .

The others are laughing and going 'ah' as though FINBAR *has caught* JACK *out.*

I'll tell yous. If you won't listen. Right? I don't have a system. And I do. I do lose a few bob every now and then. Right? So I take a little tip from Jim. And then that'll finance having a few old bets for the next few weeks. (*They laugh.*) And I've been known to have one or two wins myself, as well yous know and don't forget. I have one or two.

BRENDAN. You do not. Go on out of that you chancer.

JACK. I do.

FINBAR. I'd say the last win you had was fucking Red Rum or someone.

JACK (*aside to* VALERIE). We do be only messing like this.

FINBAR. What would anyone like? Jim?

JIM. Eh, small one, then, thanks Finbar.

FINBAR. Jack? Small one? Pint?

JACK. I'll have a small one, go on.

FINBAR. Good man. Valerie?

VALERIE. Oh no, I'm okay for the moment, thanks.

FINBAR. Are you sure? Top that up?

VALERIE. No I'm fine, honestly.

FINBAR. You're sure now?

VALERIE. No really, I'm fine.

FINBAR (*hands up*). Fair enough. We won't force you. Give us . . . eh three small ones, Brendan. Good man. Here, are you having one?

BRENDAN *is pouring three glasses of whiskey.*

BRENDAN. I'm debating whether to have one.

JACK. Ah he'll have one, go on Brendan. Who knows when the hell you'll see another drink off the Finbar fella, hah? Come on! Quick! He's all annoyed you're having one.

FINBAR (*to* VALERIE). Would you listen to him?

JACK. That fella'd peel a banana in his pocket.

JIM. Is that what that is?

They laugh.

FINBAR. First time I've been in here in ages, bringing nice company in and everything, getting this. Oh you'd have to watch the Jimmy fella. There's more going on there than he lets on. 'Is that what that is?'

BRENDAN *places the drinks on the bar.*

And look at this! Me buying the drinks and everything! Ah it's not right. What do you think Valerie?

VALERIE. Oh, it's terrible.

FINBAR. Oh, it's desperate.

He hands BRENDAN *a twenty pound note.*

There you go, Brendan. I wouldn't say you see too many twenties in here. With the boys, wouldn't be too often, I'd say. Cheers boys.

JACK. Cheers.

JIM. Good luck.

BRENDAN. Good luck now.

VALERIE. Cheers.

JACK. How did you put up with this fella showing you around?

VALERIE. Ah, he was a bit quieter today.

JACK. Well you're seeing the real him now. And I bet you prefer the other one. We've never seen it. The quiet Finbar. This one comes out at night. You see.

VALERIE. Oh, well I was getting the history of the place and everything today.

JACK. He was probably making it up on the spot. Was he?

FINBAR. Yeah. I was, that's right Jack. That's why all them photographs are fake, I had them done years ago just to fool Valerie tonight.

VALERIE (*going to the photographs*). That's all around here, is it?

FINBAR (*going to the photographs*). Yeah. That's the weir. When was that taken, Brendan?

BRENDAN. Eh. That's 1951.

FINBAR. 1951. That's your father there.

BRENDAN. Yeah. I think your father's in it too.

FINBAR. Oh he is! Valerie look at this. That's Big Finbar. .And that's Brendan's father, Paddy Byrne. This is when the ESB opened the weir.

VALERIE (*to* FINBAR). You look like your father. (*To* BRENDAN.) You don't.

FINBAR. He's like his mother. He's like the Mangans. Now . . . Who would you say that is there? In the shorts.

VALERIE. Is it you?

FINBAR. Would you go on! The big fucking head on that yoke! Excuse the language. That's Jack.

VALERIE. Oh my God! How old were you there, Jack?

JACK. Em. Oh I was about seven.

VALERIE. I wouldn't have said that was you.

FINBAR. You must be joking, you'd spot that big mutton head anywhere. The photographer nearly had to ask him to go home, there wasn't going to be room in the picture. Isn't that right, Jack?

JACK. That's right and your dad nearly climbing into the camera there.

FINBAR. He was a pillar of the community, Valerie. No one had anything against him. Except headers like your man there. (*Indicating* JACK.)

JACK. That's right Finbar. And I'm just going in here to do something up against the pillar of the community now.

JACK goes out the door at back.

FINBAR. Jays, he's a desperate fella, that one.

VALERIE. Where was this taken?

BRENDAN. That's the view of Carrick from our top field up there.

VALERIE. It's an amazing view.

FINBAR. Oh I'd say that's probably one of the best views all around here, wouldn't it be?

BRENDAN. Oh yeah I'd say so.

JIM. Oh yeah it would be, yeah.

FINBAR. You get all the Germans trekking up here in the summer, Valerie. Up from the campsite.

VALERIE. Right.

FINBAR. They do all come up – this'd be the scenic part of all around here you know. Em. There's what's . . .? There was stories all, the fairies be up there in that field. Isn't there a fort up there?

BRENDAN. There's a kind of a one.

VALERIE. A fairy fort?

FINBAR. The Germans do love all this.

BRENDAN. Well there's a . . . ring of trees, you know.

FINBAR. What's the story about the fairy road that . . . Who used to tell it?

BRENDAN. Ah, Jack'd tell you all them stories.

FINBAR. There's all this around here, Valerie, the area's steeped in old folklore, and that, you know.

BRENDAN. Jack'd know . . . the what the, you'd know a few, Jim.

JIM. Ah Jack'd tell you better than me.

FINBAR (*pointing to another photograph*). That's the Abbey now.

VALERIE. Oh yeah.

FINBAR. You can see more of it there now. What was there, Brendan? When was that?

BRENDAN. Oh, back in oh fifteen something there was a synod of bishops all came and met there, for . . . like . . . eh.

JIM. This townland used to be quite important back a few hundred years ago, Valerie. This was like the capital of the, the county, it would have been.

VALERIE. Right.

JACK *comes back in.*

FINBAR. Oh it's a very interesting place all, eh, Jack we were just saying about the, what was the story with the fairy road?

JACK. The fairy road? I go into the toilet for two minutes, I come out and you're talking about fairies. (*They laugh.*)

FINBAR. Ah, I was telling Valerie about the fort and everything. What was the story with the fairy road? Where was it?

Short pause.

JACK. Are you really interested? All the babies.

FINBAR. Ah it's a bit of fun, tell her, where was it?

JACK (*to* FINBAR). You're going to regret me saying this now, 'cause you know whose house it was?

FINBAR. Where?

JACK. It was Maura Nealon's house.

FINBAR (*self-chastising, remembering*). Oh . . . Jesus.

They laugh.

JACK. You see? That's as much cop as you have now.

FINBAR. I fucking forgot it was Maura.

JACK. These are only old stories, Valerie.

VALERIE. No. I'd like to hear it.

JACK. It's only an old cod like.

FINBAR. You're not going to be scaring the woman.

JACK. Ah it's not scary.

VALERIE. I'm interested in it.

FINBAR. You hear all old shit around here, it doesn't mean anything.

BRENDAN. This is a good little story.

JACK. It's only short. It's just. Maura . . . Nealon used come in here in the evening, sit over there at the fire. How old was she, Jim? When she died?

JIM. Oh Jays, she would have been nearly ninety.

JACK. But she was a grand, you know, spritely kind of a woman 'til the end. And she had all her . . . She was on the ball, like, you know? And she swore that this happened. When she was only a girl. She lived in that house all her life. And she had older brothers and sisters. She was the youngest. And her mother eh . . .

JIM. Bridie.

JACK. Bridie. She was a well known woman in the area. A widow woman. She was a bit of a character. Bit of a practical joker and that you know? And Maura would say that when she was young she was, Bridie was, always doing things on the older kids, hiding their . . . clothes and this, you know. And she'd tell them old fibs about what a certain, prospective boyfriend or girlfriend had said about them out on the road and this about coming courting or that. And she was always shouting from upstairs or this 'There's someone at the door.' She was always saying there's someone at the back door or there's someone coming up the path. You know. This. And there'd never be anyone there. And people got used to her. That she liked her joke.

And Maura used to say that one Saturday evening back in about 1910 or 1911, the older ones were getting ready to go out for a dance or whatever was happening. And the mother, Bridie, came down the stairs and said 'Did no one get the door?'

And they were all 'Oh here we go,' you know? And Bridie came down and *opened* the door, and there was nobody there. And she didn't say anything. And she wasn't making a big thing out of it, you know? And Maura said, she was only young, but she knew there was something wrong. She wasn't cracking the jokes. And later on when the others were all out, it was just her and her mother sitting at the fire, And her mother was very quiet. Normally she'd send Maura up to bed, early enough like. But Maura said she remembered this night because Bridie didn't send her up. She wanted someone with her, you see. And in these days, Valerie, as you know, there was no electricity out here. And there's no dark like a Winter night in the country. And there was a wind like this one tonight howling and whistling in off the sea. You hear it under the door and it's like someone singing. Singing in under the door at you. It was this type of night now.

Am I setting the scene for you?

They laugh.

Finbar's looking a bit edgy. You want to finish that small one I think.

FINBAR. Don't mind my small one. You're making very heavy weather of this yarn Jack.

JACK. Ah now, you have to enjoy it. You have to relish the details of something like this, ha?

They laugh.

So there they were, sitting there and Bridie was staring into the fire, a bit quiet. And smiling now and again at Maura, but Maura said she could see a bit of wet in her eyes. And then there was a soft knocking at the door. Someone. At the front door. And Bridie never moved. And Maura said 'Will I get the door, mammy?' And Bridie said 'No, sure, it's only someone playing a joke on us, don't mind them.' So they sat there, and there was no more knocking for a while. And em, in those days, there was no kitchen, where the extension is, Valerie, that was the back door and only a little latch on it, you know? And that's where the next knocking was. Very soft, Maura said, and very low down the door. Not like where you'd expect a grown man or a woman would be knocking, up here, you know? And again Bridie was saying, ah, it's only someone having a joke, they'll go away. And then it was at the window. Maura couldn't see anything out in the night. And her mother wouldn't let her go over. And then it stopped. But when it was late and the fire went down, Bridie wouldn't get up to get more turf for the fire. Because it was out in the shed. So they just sat there until the others came back, well after midnight.

VALERIE. What was it?

JACK. Well Maura said her mother never told the others, and one day when it was only the two of them there, a priest came and blessed the doors and the windows. And then there was no more knocking. And it was only years later that Maura heard from one of the older people in the area that the house had been built on what they call a fairy road. Like it wasn't a road, but it was a . . .

JIM. It was like a row of things.

JACK. Yeah, like a . . . From the fort up in Brendan's top field there, then the old well, and the abbey further down, and into the cove where the little pebbly beach is, there. And the . . . legend would be that the fairies would come down that way to bathe, you see. And Maura Nealon's house was built on what you'd call . . . that . . . 'road'.

VALERIE. And they wanted to come through?

JACK. Well, that'd be the idea. But Maura never heard the knocking again except on one time in the fifties when the weir was going up. There was a bit of knocking then she said. And a fierce load of dead birds all in the hedge and this, but that was it. That's the story.

FINBAR. You're not bothered by that, are you, Valerie? 'Cause it's only old cod, you know? You hear these, all around, up and down the country.

VALERIE. I think there's probably *something* in them. No I do.

JACK. Ah there might be alright. But . . . it doesn't hurt. A bit of an old story like. But I'll tell what, it'd give a thirst, like. You know? What'll yous have?

They laugh.

Valerie, top that up.

VALERIE. Em . . .

JACK. Go on.

FINBAR. Ah she will. Brendan.

BRENDAN *puts a clean tumbler on the bar.*

VALERIE. This glass is fine.

FINBAR. Oh, country ways! Good girl.

They laugh. BRENDAN *pours wine.*

JACK, Finbar. Pint?

FINBAR. Ah. Pint. Why not says you, ha?

JACK. Jim?

JIM. Ah.

JACK. Three pints please, Brendan.

BRENDAN. Three pints.

Pause. BRENDAN *works.*

FINBAR. Yep. Oh yeah.

JACK. Are you debating whether to have one yourself?

BRENDAN. I'm debating.

FINBAR. Who's winning?

BRENDAN. Ah, it's a draw. I'm going to have a glass.

FINBAR. Good man, have two, ha?

They laugh. JACK *produces his cigarettes.*

JACK. Valerie?

VALERIE. Eh, I will, thanks.

FINBAR (*pleasantly surprised*). Oh! Good girl.

JACK. Finbar?

FINBAR. No I won't, thanks Jack. Haven't had one of them fellas now, eighteen years this November.

JACK. Eighteen years, ha?

JACK *offers the pack to* BRENDAN *and* JIM *who both take one.*

FINBAR. Eighteen years. Not since I made the move. (*To* VALERIE.) Down to Carrick.

JACK (*lighting the cigarettes*). Jays, you don't look any better for it, ha?

They laugh.

FINBAR. Oh yeah? We'll see who'd look better after a round or two of the fisty footwork ha? And you with the lungs hanging out your back.

JACK. Jaysus. An auldfella like me. Ten or more years between us and you wanting to give me a few digs. Business . . . killer instinct, is it?

FINBAR. That's an eye for the gap. (*Winks at* VALERIE.) Exploit the weakness.

JACK. 'The weakness'? Sure, don't you have a grand little spooky story, about how brave you are.

FINBAR. Ah no . . .

JACK. Come on.

FINBAR. Ah that was only the . . . Walsh young one having us all on. It was only a cod, sure.

JIM. She's in America now. Niamh Walsh.

BRENDAN. It was Niamh that time, yeah?

FINBAR. Ah she was a header. Looking for attention.

VALERIE. What happened?

JACK. This was the brave fella.

FINBAR. Ah, stop. It was nothing.

JACK. This was a family lived up beside Big Finbar's place. The Walshes.

FINBAR. Ah, they were only blow-ins, he was a guard.

VALERIE. Blow-ins like me?

FINBAR. Ah no. You know what I mean.

JACK. Jays, you'll be losing business with them kind of remarks, ha? Valerie will agree with me there now.

They laugh.

FINBAR. Ah she knows what I mean. Valerie's very welcome. She knows that, don't you?

JACK. Ah leave her alone, you're embarrassing everybody now. Jaysus. (*They laugh.*) Tell her the story.

FINBAR. Ah Janey. Sure you have her in a haunted house already! She won't be able to sleep.

VALERIE. No I'd like to hear it.

FINBAR. It's not even a real one.

JACK. Ah, she wants to hear one, don't be moaning and tell her, come on.

FINBAR. Tch. Just a crowd of headbangers is all it was. There was a house out near where we were on the other side of the Knock there. It would have been the nearest place to us, Valerie, about a quarter mile down the road. And the old lad Finnerty lived on his own down there, and his family got him into a nursing home out by them down in Westport. And the people who moved in were the Walshes, your man was a sergeant in the guards, stationed in Carrick. And, like, he was fifty-odd and still only a sergeant, so, like he was no Sherlock Holmes. You know?

They laugh.

He wasn't 'Walsh of the yard' or anything like that. And they moved in. He had three daughters who were teenagers, and he had a youngfella who was married back near Longford there. So the . . . daughters were with him and the missus. And I knew them a little bit because that was the year Big Finbar died, God rest him, and they arrived about the time of the funeral so . . . you know, I met them, then. And I was living on my own because me and Big Finbar were the only two in it at the time. So I was the bachelor boy, and a gaggle of young ones after moving in next door, yo ho! You know?

They laugh.

And around that time I would have been wondering what to do, Valerie, do you know? Whether to sell it on or farm it or, you know. I was twenty-two, twenty-three, you know?

And it was, it would have been about eleven or twelve o'clock this night and there was a knock at the door and it was Mrs. Walsh. And she was all upset and asking me if I could come in, she didn't know what to do. The husband was at work out on a call, and she didn't know anyone in the area, and there was a bit of trouble. So, 'What kind of trouble?' I says. And she says she was after getting a phone call from the young one, Niamh and she was after doing the Luigi board, or what do you call it?

VALERIE. Ouija board.

FINBAR. Ouija board.

JACK. 'Luigi board!' She was down there in the chipper in Carrick, was she, Finbar?

FINBAR. Ah fuck off. I meant the Ouija board. You know what I meant. She was after being down in . . .

JACK. 'The Luigi board.'

FINBAR. She was after, come on now, she was after being down in a friend of hers house or this. And they were after doing the . . . Ouija board. And she phoned her mother to come and collect her. They *said* they were after getting a spirit or this, you know, and she was scared, saying it was after her. And I just obviously thought, this was a load of bollocks, you know.

If you'll . . . excuse the language Valerie, but here was the
mother saying she d gone and picked her up. I mean, like sorry,
but I think it was all a bit mad. But on the way back they'd seen
something, like the mother had seen it as well. Like a dog on
the road, running with the car and running after it. Like there's
dogs all around here, Valerie, you know? The farmers have
them. There was a big dog up there, Jack, that Willie
McDermott had that time.

JACK. Oh, Jaysus, yeah, it was like a, if you saw it from the
distance, you'd think it was a little horse. It was huge.

JIM. Saxon.

FINBAR. That was it. Saxon.

JIM. It was an Irish Wolfhound. He got it off a fella in the North.

FINBAR. Yeah, it was huge; you'd be used to seeing dogs all
around the place. All kinds, but they'd be tame, like. Their
bark 'd be worse than their bite. So I wasn't too . . . taken with
this story. But she wanted me to come down because when
they'd got back to the house, the young one, Niamh, was going
hysterical saying there was something on the stairs. Like no one
else could see it. But she could, she said there was a woman,
looking at her. And Mrs. Walsh didn't know what to do. They
couldn't contact the hubbie, and would I come down? I mean,
what made her think there was anything I could do, I don't
know. But she was panicking, you know . . . So I got in the car
and we went down. And Jesus, now, I've never seen the like of
it. The young one was in . . . bits. They had a blanket around
her and she was as white, now as . . . (*Points to* JACK's *shirt.*)
as white as that. Well, whiter because that's probably filthy.

JACK. Ha ha.

FINBAR. But I'm not messing. And she wouldn't come out of the
living room. Because she said there was a woman on the stairs.
And I said, what's the woman doing? And she said, 'She's just
looking at me.' She was terrified. Now I didn't know whether
she was after taking drugs or drink or what she was after doing.
So I says to phone for Dr. Joe in Carrick. This is Joe Dillon,
Valerie, you'd see him in the town, he still has his surgery there
beside the Spar. Very nice fella. And I got through to him, and
he was on his way, and the Niamh one was shouting at me to
close the living room door. Because I was out in the hall where
the phone was, and she could see the woman looking at her
over the banister. Like, she was that bad, now. So Mrs. Walsh
phoned Fr. Donal, got him out of bed. And fair dues, like, he

came down. And he sort of blessed the place a little bit. Like,
he'd be more Vatican Two. There wouldn't be much of all the
demons or that kind of carry-on with him.

JACK. Jaysus, sure, he'd collapse. He's like that. (*JACK holds up
his little finger.*) Him and a demon . . .

They laugh.

FINBAR. But Dr. Joe gave her a sedative and off she went then,
you know. And we all had a little drink, and poor Mrs. Walsh
was understandably, very, you know, shaken and everything.
But Fr. Donal told her not to mind the Ouija, and it was only an
old cod. And it was Niamh's imagination and this. And then,
the phone rang, right? And it was the youngfella, the brother
who was married in Longford. And he was all, that his baby
was crying and he had it out of the cot and he was standing at
the window and he saw a dead neighbour, of theirs out in the
garden. A grown man. Ringing his mammy.

VALERIE. Out in the garden?

FINBAR. Standing out in the garden. Looking at the house, some
old dear who'd died, a few weeks before. I mean, now either,
they were all headers in that family or I'm, you know? And . . .
when I went home then, that night, I was sitting at the fire
having a last fag before the sack, and, Jack would know the
house, the stairs come down into the, the main room. And I
had my back to it, to the stairs, and it's stupid now, but at the
time . . . I couldn't turn around. I couldn't get up to go to bed.
Because I thought there was something on the stairs. (*Low
laugh.*) And I just sat there, looking at an empty fireplace. And
I sat there until it got bright. I was like a boy, you know? I
wouldn't in case something saw me. You know that way. I
wouldn't even light another fag. Like I was dying for one, and
I wouldn't . . . mad. But when it was bright then, I was grand,
you know? Obviously there was nothing there and everything,
but that was the last fag I ever had. (*Short pause.*) They moved
away then, though, after that, the Walshes. (*Pause.*) Yep.

VALERIE. And was that when you moved . . . down to Carrick?

FINBAR. Yeah. (*Nods slowly.*) Maybe that . . . had something to
do with it. I don't know.

VALERIE. Mmm.

JACK. Moving down into the lights, yeah?

FINBAR. Mmm. Might be. Might be alright. Didn't want the
loneliness maybe, you know? (*Pause.*) Yous all think I'm a

lulah now. (*They laugh.*) Ha? I'm the header, says you, ha? I'm going to powder my nose I think. (*He goes out back.*)

JACK (*calling after him*). Sure we knew you were a headbanger. Knew that all along.

They laugh. Pause.

Yeah.

VALERIE. I'd imagine, though, it can get very quiet.

JACK. Oh it can yeah. Ah you get used to it. Brendan.

BRENDAN. Ah yeah you don't think about it.

JACK. Me and Brendan are the fellas on our own. Jim has the mammy to look after, but we're, you know, you can come in here in the evenings. During the day you'd be working. You know, there's company around. Bit of a community all spread around the place, like.

JIM. You can put the radio on.

Pause.

JACK. Have you got any plans or that, for . . . here?

VALERIE. Not really, I'm just going to try and have some . . .

JACK. Peace and quiet.

VALERIE. Mm.

JACK. Jaysus, you're in the right place, so, ha?

They laugh.

You're going to have a peace and quiet . . . over . . . load. Oh yeah.

BRENDAN. Sure, you can always stick the head in here. Or Jack, or me or whatever, be able to sort you out for anything.

VALERIE. Thanks. I should be okay.

JACK. You're only ten minutes up the road. And Jaysus, by the looks of things you'll have a job keeping Finbar away. Ha?

VALERIE. Ah he's a dote.

JACK. Jays, I never heard him called that before, ha? Lots of other things, never that though.

FINBAR *comes back.*

FINBAR. What have you fecking heard? What are you talking about this time, Mullen, ha? About how twenty Germans were

poisoned by the drink in here, last Summer. (*Winks at*
BRENDAN.) Ha?

JACK. No, I'd say the Arms is the place where that kind of carry
on happens. You'd get a pint in there now, I believe, that'd put
you on your back for a fortnight.

FINBAR. Don't mind them, Valerie, they're only jealous.

VALERIE. That's probably what it is, alright.

FINBAR. You see now? At least there's one person on my side.

JACK .Yeah. You. She's only sticking up for you to make sure she
gets a lift after you scaring the living daylights out of her with
your insistence on spooky stories.

FINBAR. Go on. It's only headers like me get a fright like that,
ha? Fecking lulahs.

They laugh. JIM *counts some money.*

JIM. Does eh . . . is anybody?

JACK. Ah no, Jim, I'm grand, you look after yourself.

JIM. Are you sure? Valerie?

VALERIE. No I'll get you one.

FINBAR. Ah, no Valerie, you're . . .

JACK (*simultaneously*). No, you're alright.

FINBAR. You're the guest. You're the guest.

JIM. Will you have a small one, Finbar?

FINBAR. Eh no, Jim. Thanks very much. I'm fine for the moment,
finish this pint.

BRENDAN. Small one, Jim?

JIM. Thanks Brendan. I'll eh, I'll just lash a bit of turf on that,
will I?

FINBAR. Good man, Jim.

BRENDAN *gives* JIM *his drink.* JIM *leaves money on the bar
and goes to the fire, leaving his drink on the mantel.*

JACK. Keep the chill out, ha?

FINBAR. This is it.

FINBAR *looks at his watch.*

VALERIE. Do you want to?

FINBAR. Ah no, no, no. I'm just watching the time. We've a
    wedding tomorrow.

VALERIE. Would you be . . . directly . . . working in the hotel?

JACK. Saves him paying someone's wages.

FINBAR. Sure that's how I have it, boy. (*He winks at* VALERIE.)

JACK. We know.

FINBAR. No. There's certain things I'd do myself on a big day.
    One of the first things I ever learned in the business. The
    importance of good stock.

VALERIE. Soup stock?

FINBAR. For the soup. For the gravy, for the sauces, ah, you use it
    all over the place. And it's just a little thing I do. A little ritual.
    In the morning, I help do the stock. What do we have from
    yesterday, and so on. A little mad thing I do, but there you are.

VALERIE. I think that's lovely.

FINBAR. Ah, it's a little thing I do. Little superstition. These'll
    tell you. I'm famous for it.

JACK. It's a gimmick.

BRENDAN. Who's getting married, Finbar?

FINBAR. Do you know Nuala Donnelly? 'Nu' they call her. She
    used to work for me in the Arms. Declan Donnelly's girl. Gas
    young one.

BRENDAN. Oh yeah.

FINBAR. You used to be pals with Declan, Jim.

JIM. Poor Declan. Be ten years dead in July. God rest him. Lovely
    fella.

FINBAR. She's a gas young one, the daughter. 'Nu' they call her.
    'Call me "Nu",' she says, the first day she was working for me.
    Not afraid to speak up for herself or anything. Used to tell us
    who was having affairs and all this. She was chambermaid, you
    see. She knew the couples who were being all illicit because
    she'd go in to do the room in the morning and the bed would be
    already made. The woman in the affair would have done it out
    of guilt, you see. Cover it all up, for herself as much as for
    anyone else. She's a mad young one.

VALERIE. Would you get many people using the hotel like that?

FINBAR. Not at all. I wouldn't say so. But Nuala just you know, she's a gabber and a talker.

JIM (*at fire*). Who's she getting married to Finbar?

FINBAR. Oh Jesus some fella from out the country. He must be in his forties. Shame, a young one getting hitched to an old fella like that. He must have plenty of money. (*To* VALERIE.) Be like getting married to that. (*Indicating* JACK.) He's a nice stash hidden away in that little garage, I'll tell you. Hoping to trap some little thing with it. Isn't that right, Jack?

JACK. That's my plan.

FINBAR. But you'd want to be careful of the old lads living on their own. They've a big pot of stew constantly on the heat, and they just keep throwing a few old bits of scraps in it every couple of days. And they survive off that, don't you Jack? That'd do you.

JACK. It's a feast every day.

FINBAR. Aw. Dreadful fellas. And then they manage to get a girl and the dust'd be like that on everything. And your man'd be after living in two rooms all his life, and the poor young one would have to get in and clean it all out. Thirty years of old newspapers and cheap thrillers, all lying there in the damp since their mammies died and that was the last bit of cleaning went on in the place. That right Jack?

JACK. That's us to a tee.

BRENDAN. Jaysus, speak for yourself, ha?

FINBAR. Oh, they'd be desperate men. Changing the sheets in the bed every Christmas. And there'd be soot all over everything, and bits of rasher, and egg and pudding on the floor.

VALERIE. The poor girl.

FINBAR. The poor girl is right. So the least I can do is make sure her reception, in the Arms, is a little memory for her to have in the future, in the cold nights. Cheers.

They have all enjoyed this.

JACK. You've a terrible warped mind, do you know that?

FINBAR (*winks at* VALERIE). Sure I'm only telling it like it is, ha?

JIM. Nuala getting married. You don't feel the time.

FINBAR. No.

JIM. Mm. I remember, oh, it must have been twenty or more years ago, doing a job with him. Declan. Talking about what we were saying earlier. The priest over in Glen was looking for a couple of lads to do a bit of work. And he was down in Carrick in the Arms. He'd, come over, from Glen. You know? Which was an odd thing anyway. Like what was he doing coming over all the way just to get a couple of young fellas? But Declan Donnelly got put onto him. There was a few quid and he knocked up to me and we were to go over to the church in Glen the following day. And I remember I was dying with the 'flu and I had a terrible high temperature. The mother was telling me to stay in the leaba. Burn it off. But like it was a couple of quid on the Q.T. so I told Declan, yeah, I'd do it tomorrow. No problem. And then the next day it was lashing rain. I'll never forget it. He called for me in his dad's car. The smell of sheep in it like you wouldn't believe. God, it would kill you. He used to put them in the car, chauffeur them around, you know?

Smiles.

And we drove over to Glen. And the priest took us into the Sacristy, and the job, of all things was to dig a grave in the yard. That day was the removal of the remains and they needed the grave for the morning.

And fair dues, like, Declan said it to him. Was there no one else around the place could have done it? And the priest got a bit cagey and he was saying something about the local boys being busy with a game of Gaa, or something. And the rain was pelting down and he gave us leggings and wellies and the whole bit they had there and a couple of shovels. And then he put up his umbrella all annoyed, like, and he brought us out, over to a grave under a tree. It was a family one and there were two down in it already, the mother and the father, and this was going to be for the boy. Well, he was a man, like, a middle-aged fella. But there was two in it so we wouldn't have to go down for miles, like. So he went off to do his business and get ready, and me and Declan got stuck in. And with the rain and all, I was dying with the 'flu. My arms were sore and then my legs got sore. And then my neck got sore. And I was boiling. But we got down two, two and a half foot and we took a break. We got in Declan's car and he pulled out a bottle of poitín. I couldn't eat, but I had a good belt of the bottle, like. Knocked me into some sort of shape.

And we just sat there for a while, listening to the radio, and the rain coming down, and then we got out and got stuck in again. Having a swig every half hour or so, keeping it going. And we

saw the hearse arrive then. And the mad thing was there was
only about two or three other fellas there for the service. Of
course the removal is only a short thing mostly, but to have no
one there, and for a man who's not an old man, it was funny,
you know? And then that was over and the priest came out to
us. We were nearly finished. And he just cleared us for the
funeral in the morning, and then he went off. So me and Declan
were the only two there then.

Short pause.

And your man was laid out in the church. And Declan went off
to get a tarp to stretch . . . over . . . the grave, and I put a big
lump of a door over it. And I was just waiting on Declan and
having the last drop, under the tree, dying to get in out of the
rain, and thinking maybe we'd stick the head in somewhere for
a quick pint on the way back. You know? And then, I saw this,
fella, come out of the church. And he walked straight over to
me. He was in a suit so I reckoned he was . . . paying his
respects or whatever. And over he comes, through the
gravestones. And he was looking around him a bit, like he
didn't know the place. And he stood beside me, under the tree,
looking at the grave. I didn't know what to say, you know? And
he goes, 'Is this for so and so?' I forget the name. And I go,
'That's right, yeah.' And he says, 'That's the wrong grave.'
And I'm like, 'No. This is where the priest said, like.' And he
looked at me breathing hard, through his nose. Like he was
holding his temper. And he goes, 'Come on, I'll show you.'
And he walks off. And, I was all like 'fuck this' you know?
And I was cursing Declan, waiting for him to come back. And
your man turns around, you know 'Come on, it's over here.'
I just, he was a lulah, you know? And I was nearly climbing
into the grave myself, with the tiredness. And I was sick. So I
followed him just to get it over with. And he stopped at a grave.
Like a new enough one. A white one with a picture of a little
girl on it.

And he says, 'It's this one, here.' And I just went, 'Okay, right
you are mister, I'll have it done, no problem. See you now.'
And he . . . sort of touched the gravestone and he went off, back
into the church. I was breathing a few sighs of relief, I'll tell
you. And Declan came back with the tarp and I said,' Did you
see your man?' And he didn't know what I was talking about.
So I told him and all this, and we just kind of had a bit of a
laugh at it. And we just got out of there. Stopped into the Green
Man on the way back for a few pints and that night, my fever
broke. But I was knackered. The mother wouldn't let me go to

the burial. Declan did it on his own I think. But I was laid up for a couple of days. And one day the mother brought me in the paper and on the obituaries, there was a picture of your man whose grave we'd dug. And you know what I'm going to say. It was the spit of your man I'd met in the graveyard. So I thought first it was a brother or a relative or someone, I'd met. And I forgot about it a bit and didn't think about it for ages until one night Declan told me he'd found out why the priest from Glen was looking for a couple of Carrick fellas, for the job.

The fella who'd died had had a bit of a reputation for 'em, being a pervert. And Jesus, when I heard that you know? If it was him. And he wanted to go down in the grave with the . . . little girl. Even after they were gone. It didn't bear . . . thinking about. It came back when you said about Declan's girl. Yeah.

Pause.

FINBAR. Jaysus, Jim. That's a terrible story to be telling.

JIM. Well, you know. I was very sick and we'd had the few little drinks. From Dick Lenihan's batch, you know?

JACK. Oh Jesus. Firewater. Sure that'd put a hole in the glass, let alone give you hallucinations.

A little laugh. Pause.

VALERIE. Do you think it was a, an hallucination Jim?

JIM. God I don't know. I was flying like, but it was some coincidence him showing me where he wanted to be buried. And me knowing nothing about him like.

VALERIE. Mm. (*Nods.*)

FINBAR. Are you alright, Valerie? (*Little laugh.*) You look a bit peaky there.

VALERIE. No, I'm fine. Just, actually is the Ladies out this way?

BRENDAN. Ah. (*Short pause.*) Jays, I'll tell you what, Valerie, this is very embarrassing but the Ladies is busted. And with the . . . (JACK *laughs.*) I'm getting it fixed for the Germans like, but I haven't done it yet.

FINBAR. Ah, you're a terrible man, Brendan.

BRENDAN. No, I'll bring you in the house, come on.

VALERIE. Are you sure?

BRENDAN. Aw yeah, yeah, no problem.

JACK. Don't worry Valerie, if you're not back in ten minutes we'll come and get you, ha?

BRENDAN. Jaysus. Give it a rest. Come on, Valerie, I'll put the lights on for you. Out this way.

FINBAR. Bye now.

VALERIE. Bye.

BRENDAN *and* VALERIE *leave by door, back.*

Pause.

JACK. Yep. (*Short pause.*)

FINBAR (*to* JIM). Jaysus. That's some fucking story. To be telling a girl, like. Perverts out in the country. For fuck's sake.

Short pause.

JACK. Like your story had nothing in it, ha?

FINBAR. Ah that was only old headers in it.

JACK. But you brought the whole thing up. With the fairies. The fairies! She's in that house.

FINBAR. I forgot it was that house. I forgot it was Maura Nealon. It was an honest mistake.

JACK. Honest mistake.

FINBAR. What.

JACK. Don't be giving it that old cod now.

FINBAR. What do you mean?

JACK. With bringing her around and all.

FINBAR. What about it?

JACK. Bringing her up the head and all. (*Short pause.*)

FINBAR. Yeah?

JACK. So don't be giving it the old cod now.

FINBAR. What cod, Jack? (*Pause.*) I'm asking you. (*Short pause.*) What?

JIM. Ah boys, we have a small one. Come on now.

FINBAR. Hang on a minute, Jim. What?

JACK. Well you get me to tell a story about the house she's in.

FINBAR. I didn't *know* that though. I told you that.

JACK. Whatever. And then you tell the story about the Walsh girl.

FINBAR. Sure it was you told me to say that.

JACK. What?

FINBAR. Talking about the fags and giving up the fags and all that. When you offered them that time.

JACK. Would you cop on? 'Ghosts' and 'giving up the fags'.

FINBAR. Okay. I'm sorry. What? I regret the stories, then. I don't think we should have any more of them. But that's what I'm saying, like.

JIM. I didn't think. I just said it. With Declan Donnelly and that. It just, you know . . .

FINBAR. Ah no no no. Jim. We're not blaming anybody. I regret it now. And just let's not have any more of them, and that's all.

JACK. Oh, you regret it now?

FINBAR. Yeah.

JACK. It's not part of the tour.

FINBAR. Ah now, come on.

JACK. Bit of local colour.

FINBAR. No. Jack.

JACK. Just don't berate Jim for telling a story after you telling one yourself.

FINBAR. I apologise, if that's what I did. Sorry Jim. Now, I'll say that. But stop with this . . . tour guide thing. That's not fair. The woman's moved out here on her own. For some reason. There's something obviously going on . . . in her life. I'm just trying to make it easier for her. Give her a welcome, for fuck's sake. So don't . . . be implying anything else. I don't like it. (*Pause.*) I've apologised to Jim. And I'm saying no more stories. (*Short pause.*) Sure I'm married! I mean really. Yous are the single boys. (*Short pause. Warm.*) Sure I can't remember the last time I saw a suit on you.

Pause.

JACK. Oh now it's me?

JIM. Ah now boys, come on. That's enough. That's enough of that.

JACK. You think I have intentions, is it?

FINBAR. I didn't know. You're entitled.

JACK. I do often wear a suit. Don't come in here for the first time in God knows, thinking we're fucking hicks. 'Cause you're from round here.

Pause.

FINBAR. Nobody's saying that. You've got the wrong idea, Jack. And it's not worth falling out over. Now, I'll buy you a drink. And that'll be the fucking end of it now. Alright?

JACK. You will not buy me a fucking drink. (*Short pause.*) I'll buy *you* one, and *that'll* be the end of it.

He extends his hands. They shake.

JIM. That's more like it, men. That's more like it, ha?

JACK goes behind the bar.

JACK. What'll yous have?

FINBAR (*offering hand to* JIM). Sorry Jim.

JIM. Ah no no no. Stop. (*Shaking hands.*) It's forgotten.

JACK. Finbar.

FINBAR. Ah. I think I'll just have a glass, Jack, I think.

JACK. Ah, you'll have a small one with that.

FINBAR. Jays, you'll fucking kill me now, ha? I think he's trying to kill me Jim, is he?

JIM. Oh now.

JACK. Jim?

JIM. Small one, Jack, thanks.

JACK. You'll have a little pint with that, I think.

JIM. Go on, ha?

FINBAR. Ah good man. (*Pause.*) Jays. That was a hot one there for a minute, ha?

JACK. We'll say no more about it. We might tell a few jokes when she comes back. (*They laugh.*)

FINBAR. Jays. This is it. How's the mammy, Jim?

JIM. Ah, do you know what it is? She's just old. And everything's going on her.

FINBAR. Ah Jaysus, ha? I'll have to get up and see her.

JACK. I was saying that earlier. It would be the time, you think, Jim.

JIM. Ah.

FINBAR. She does be alright on her own, with you coming out for an old jar or that?

JIM. Oh don't mind her. She's well able to tell you what's what. The only thing would be the eyes, but she's the one, I'm always mixing up the tablets.

She knows exactly what she's supposed to be taking when. So. But we have the telly in that room. And she'll listen to that and drop off.

FINBAR. Well that's alright, isn't it?

JIM. Oh she's still . . . I'm taking her over tomorrow to see her sister in the, in the order.

JACK. That's a closed order, Jim, yeah?

JIM. Yeah, you know. They don't talk and all that. But the sister is six years older than the mammy, now, you know, so?

FINBAR. Gas. She'll be alright for the drive?

JIM. Oh, she'll be knackered, she'll be out like a light when we get back.

FINBAR. Ah.

JIM. Ah, yeah.

BRENDAN *and* VALERIE *come back.*

BRENDAN. So this was all the original. Before the house.

VALERIE. Right.

FINBAR. There you are, we thought we were going to have to send out a search party.

VALERIE. I was having a good nosy around.

FINBAR. Wasn't too much of a state, no?

VALERIE. Tidier than I normally am.

JACK. That's he had the sisters over today. That's all that is.

FINBAR. I saw them having their lunch in my place today.

BRENDAN. Don't be talking.

FINBAR (*gingerly*). Oh . . . back off there. Sensitive area. Eh, Valerie, darling, I don't want you to be stranded here with me now if I'm keeping you.

BRENDAN. Sure we can look after her.

FINBAR. Ah no, I'm grand for a while yet.

VALERIE. I, em. Hearing about. All these . . . you know, stories. It's . . .

FINBAR. Ah that's the end of them, now. We've had enough of them old stories, they're only an old cod. We've just been joking about it there when you were out. We'll all be witless, ha? We won't be able to sleep in our beds!

VALERIE. No, see, something happened to me. That just hearing you talk about it tonight. It's important to me. That I'm not . . . bananas.

I mean, I'm a fairly straight . . . down the line . . . person. Working. I had a good job at D.C.U. I had gone back to work after having my daughter, Niamh. My husband is a teacher at D.C.U. We had Niamh in 1988. And I went back to work when she was five, when she started school. And we'd leave her with Daniel's parents, my husband's parents. His mother always picked her up from school. And I'd collect her after work. And last year she, she was dying to learn how to swim. And the school had a thing. They'd take the class down to the C.R.C. in Clontarf on Wednesdays. She was learning very well. No problem. Loved the water. She couldn't wait for Wednesdays and swimming. Daniel used to take her to the pool on Saturdays and everything.

But for such a bright, outgoing, happy girl she was a big em . . . She had a problem sleeping at night. She was afraid of the dark. She never wanted you to leave the room.

One of us would have to lie there with her until she went off, and even when she did, she'd often have to come in and sleep with us.

And I'd say to her, 'What's wrong, when you go to bed?' But in the daytime, you know, she wouldn't care. Night time was a million years away. And she wouldn't think about it. But at night there were people at the window, there were people in the attic, there was someone coming up the stairs. There were children knocking, in the wall. And there was always a man standing across the road who she'd see. Like there was loads of things. The poor thing. I wanted to bring her to a doctor, but Daniel said she'd grow out of it. And we should be careful, just, about books we got her, and what she saw on the telly and all of this.

But I mean, she used to be even be scared that when she got up in the morning that Mammy and Daddy would have gone away and she'd be in the house on her own. That was one she told Daniel's mother. And all the furniture and carpets and everything would be gone. I mean, you know? So I told her after that, you know, we'd never, you know, it was ridiculous. And that if she was scared or worried at all during the day to ring me, and I'd come and get her, and there was nothing to worry about. And she knew our number, she was very good at learning numbers off and everything. She knew ours and her nana's and mine at work. She knew them all.

But then, in March, last year, the school had a, a sponsored swim, and the kids were going to swim a length of the pool. And I promised I was going to go and watch her. But I got . . . I was late, out of work, and I was only going to be in time to meet her afterwards, but em, when I got there . . . There was an ambulance and I thought, like, the pool is in the Central Remedial Clinic, so I thought like it was just somebody being dropped there. I didn't really pay any attention.

But when I got in, I saw that there was no one in the pool and one of the teachers was there with a group of kids. And she was crying and some of the children were crying. And this woman, another one of the mums came over and said there'd been an accident. And Niamh had hit her head in the pool and she'd been in the water and they had been trying to resuscitate her. But she said she was going to be alright. And I didn't believe it was happening. I thought it must have been someone else. And I went into, I was brought into, a room and Niamh was on a table. It was a table for table-tennis, and an ambulance man was giving her the . . . kiss of life.

She was in her bathing suit. And the ambulance man said he didn't think that what he was doing was working. And he didn't know if she was alive. And he wrapped her in a towel and carried her out to the ambulance. And I got in the back with him. And they radioed on ahead, they were going to put her on a machine in Beaumont and try to revive her there. But the ambulance man knew, I think. She wasn't breathing, and he just knew and he said if I wanted to just say goodbye to her in the ambulance in case I didn't get a chance in the hospital.

And I gave her a little hug. She was freezing cold. And I told her Mammy loved her very much. She just looked asleep but her lips were gone blue and she was dead.

And it had happened so fast. Just a few minutes. And I don't think I have to tell you. How hard it was. Between me and Daniel, as well. It didn't seem real. At the funeral I just thought I could go and lift her out of the coffin and that would be the end of all this.

I think Daniel was. I don't know if he actually, blamed me, there was nothing I could do. But he became very busy in his work. Just. Keeping himself . . . em. But I was, you know, I was more, just I didn't really know what I was doing. Just walking around or sitting in the house, with Daniel's mother, fussing around the place.

Just, months of this. Not really talking about it, like.

Pause.

But, and then one morning. I was in bed, Daniel had gone to work. I usually lay there for a few hours, trying to stay asleep, really, I suppose. And the phone rang. And I just left it. I wasn't going to get it. And it rang for a long time. Em, eventually it stopped, and I was dropping off again. But then it started ringing again, for a long time. So I thought it must have been Daniel trying to get me. Someone who knew I was there.

So I went down and answered it. And. The line was very faint. It was like a crossed line. There were voices, but I couldn't hear what they were saying. And then I heard Niamh. She said, 'Mammy?' And I . . . just said, you know? 'Yes?' And she said . . . she wanted me to come and collect her.

I mean, I wasn't sure whether this was a dream or her leaving us had been a dream. I just said 'Where are you?'

And she said she thought she was at Nana's. In the bedroom. But Nana wasn't there. And she was scared. There were children knocking in the walls and the man was standing across the road, and he was looking up and he was going to cross the road. And could I come and get her?

And I said I would, of course I would. And I dropped the phone and I ran out to the car in just a tee-shirt I slept in. And I drove to Daniel's mother's house. And I could hardly see, I was crying so much. I mean, I knew she wasn't going to be there. I knew she was gone. But to think wherever she was . . . that . . . And there was nothing I could do about it. Daniel's mother had to get a doctor and I . . . slept for a day or two. But it was . . . Daniel felt that I . . . needed to face up to Niamh being gone. But I just thought he should face up to what happened to me. He was insisting I got some 'treatment' and then . . . everything would be okay. But you know, what can help that, if she's out there? She still . . . she still needs me. (*Pause.*)

JACK. You don't think it could have been a dream you were having, no? (*Short pause.*)

VALERIE. I heard her. (*Short pause.*)

FINBAR. Sure, you were after getting a terrible shock, Valerie. These things can happen. Your brain is . . . trying to deal with it, you know? (*Pause.*) Is your husband going to . . . come down?

VALERIE. I don't think so.

FINBAR. Ah, it'd be a terrible shame if you don't . . . if you didn't see him because of something as, as, you know . . . that you don't even know what it was. (*Short pause.*)

BRENDAN. She said she knew what it was.

FINBAR. But, sure you can't just accept that, that you, you know . . . I mean . . . surely you, you have to look at the broader thing of it here.

JIM. It might have been a wrong number.

BRENDAN. What?

JIM. It could have been a wrong number or something wrong with the phone, you know? And you'd think you heard it. Something on the line.

BRENDAN. But you wouldn't hear someone's voice on the fucking thing, Jim.

JIM. Just it might have been something else.

JACK. Here, go easy, Brendan, Jim's only trying to talk about the fucking thing.

FINBAR. Ah lads.

JACK. Just take it easy.

VALERIE. Stop. I don't want . . . it's something that happened. And it's nice just to be here and . . . hear what you were saying. I know I'm not crazy.

FINBAR. Valerie, love, nobody's going to think that. But . . . just . . . no one knows about these things, sure, they're not real even. You hear all sorts of old cod, all round. But there's usually some kind of . . . explanation for it. Sure, Jim said himself he was delirious with the 'flu that time. Jim.

JIM. I had a right temperature.

FINBAR. Maura . . . eh . . . Nealon, sure she was in here every night of the week. Brendan. About how much would she drink? Be honest now.

BRENDAN. How much did she drink?

JACK. Have a bit of respect, Finbar.

FINBAR. I'm trying to make a point, Jack. The woman was a drinker.

JACK. We're all drinkers.

FINBAR. But, come on. She was an alcoholic, Valerie. She used have a bottle of whiskey put away before you knew where you were. Sure, who wouldn't be hearing knocking on the door after that?

JACK. Ah you're not being fair on her now. The woman's dead, she can't defend herself.

FINBAR. I'm not casting anything on her. If she came in that door now, if she was alive, I'd be buying her drink, and more power to her, I'd hope she'd enjoy it. I'd be the first to buy her a drink. But I run a bar myself down in the Arms. I know all about what a right few drinks'll do to you. She liked her drop is what I'm saying.

BRENDAN. What about you? And the Walshes?

FINBAR. Look. How many times do I have to say it? They were all a bunch of fucking headers!

Pause.

I got the wind put up me that night. Fair enough. But that's what these stories do. But I resent that now. What I went through that night. But I was only young. And that's over with. Fucking headbangers.

Pause.

And after all that, I'm ignoring the bigger thing, I'm very sorry about your daughter, Valerie, I'm very sorry indeed.

JACK. Oh we all are. Of course we are. It's terrible.

Long pause.

FINBAR. I'm going to have to go, I'm afraid. I don't want to, but . . .

VALERIE . Okay.

BRENDAN. Ah here, I'll leave her down.

FINBAR. But you might want to come on now, no?

VALERIE. Em.

BRENDAN. Ah, have another drink and relax for a little while.

VALERIE. Yeah, I think I'm going to hang on for another little while.

FINBAR. Are you going to go easy on the old stories?

JACK. Ah stop being an old woman. She'll be grand.

FINBAR. Alright?

JACK. She'll be grand.

JIM. Could I get a lift, Finbar?

FINBAR. Of course you can, Jim.

JACK. You're okay for Father Donal's car in the morning?

JIM (*counting money*). No problem. I'll be there about quarter to nine.

JACK. Grand, just, I've got to get out to Conor Boland.

JIM. Yeah. It's fine. Brendan, em . . .

BRENDAN. Naggin?

JIM. Please.

BRENDAN *puts a small bottle of whiskey in a plastic bag and gives it to* JIM.

FINBAR. Yep.

JIM. Well. Valerie.

VALERIE. It was very nice to meet you.

JIM (*taking her hand*). I'm very sorry about what's happened to you. And I'm sure your girl is quite safe and comfortable wherever she is, and I'm going to say a little prayer for her, but I'm sure she doesn't need it. She's a saint. She's a little innocent. And that fella I saw in the churchyard that time was only the rotten poitín and the fever I had. Finbar's right. You enjoy your peace and quiet here now. And we'll see you again. You're very nice. Goodnight now.

VALERIE. Goodnight. Thanks Jim.

JIM. That's alright.

FINBAR. Valerie. (*He takes her hand.*)

VALERIE. Thanks for everything.

FINBAR. My pleasure, darling. And I'll call up to you now in the next day or two . . .

VALERIE. Fine.

FINBAR. And we'll make sure you're all right and you're settling in with us. You're very welcome.

He kisses her awkwardly on the cheek.

VALERIE. Thanks for everything, Finbar.

FINBAR. That's quite alright. Men.

JACK. Finbar.

FINBAR. I'll see you soon, I hope, Jack.

They shake hands.

FINBAR. Alright?

JACK. See you soon.

FINBAR. Brendan.

BRENDAN. Take it easy now, Finbar. Look after yourself.

FINBAR. I won't leave it so long next time.

BRENDAN. Okay.

JIM. Goodnight.

BRENDAN. Goodnight Jim.

VALERIE. See you soon.

JACK. See you in the morning.

JIM. Quarter to nine.

FINBAR. See yous now.

   JIM *and* FINBAR *leave.*

JACK. There you are now.

BRENDAN. Mm.

JACK. I'm sorry for snapping that time.

BRENDAN. Ah no. Sure. I was . . .

VALERIE. I think it was my fault.

JACK. Would you go on? Of course it wasn't your fault. You know, it's all very well, us sitting around, fecking about with

these old stories. But then, for something personal like that.
That's happened to you. People are, going to deal with it in
different ways. Jim, was . . . you know . . .

BRENDAN. Yeah . . .

JACK. He didn't mean anything.

BRENDAN. He didn't really mean there was anything wrong with
your phone, I don't think.

They laugh a little. Pause.

JACK. It's em . . . a terrible thing that happened. Do you ever
get over something like that, I wonder? I don't mean the . . .
phone . . . call, you know.

VALERIE. I know. (*Pause.*) I don't know. (*Pause.*)

JACK. We're very sorry.

BRENDAN. Come on we sit at the fire. It's getting cold. We'll
have a last one.

JACK. Good idea.

BRENDAN. Give us your glass, Valerie. Jack, you'll have a small
one, for the road.

VALERIE. Can I get this?

JACK. Ah no no no.

BRENDAN. It's on the house now. Bar's officially closed. Go on.

JACK *and* VALERIE *move to the fire.*

JACK. You get yourself in there now. We'll be grand in a minute.

BRENDAN. I'm going to give you a little brandy, Valerie. This
wine is freezing in the fridge.

JACK. Good man.

VALERIE. Oh lovely. Thanks.

JACK. Good girl. That's it now. (*To* BRENDAN.) Jim'll be in a
bad way, all the same when the mammy goes, what do you
think Brendan?

BRENDAN Oh definitely. She's been very sick, Valerie, for years
now. Fading fast, like, for years! She still spoils that boy rotten,
ha? Though.

JACK. Oh definitely. Oh yeah.

BRENDAN *brings the drinks over.*

VALERIE. That's an awful lot.

BRENDAN. Ah it's not really.

JACK. There's no law says you have to drink it all, ha? Your man does put it back in the bottle.

BRENDAN. Would you ever fuck off?

JACK. I think we should drink this to you, sweetheart.

BRENDAN. Yes. To Valerie.

JACK. Hope it's all . . . (*Raises glass.*) In the end . . .

BRENDAN. Cheers.

VALERIE. Cheers.

They drink.

VALERIE. You've no children, Jack, no?

JACK. No, darling, never married. But I do be telling this fella to be on the lookout. A young fella like him to end up like me.

VALERIE. Do you wish you had married?

JACK. Sure who'd have me? A cantankerous old fucker like me.

BRENDAN. Too right.

JACK. Yeah . . . it's a thing, you know? I do say it to Brendan. I'm down in the garage. And the fucking tin roof on the thing. On my own on that country road. You see it was bypassed by the main road into Carrick. And there's no . . . like in the summer the heat has the place like an oven, with the roof, or if it's not that, it's the rain pelting down on it like bricks, the noise of it. You've heard it Brendan. You can't even hear the radio anymore. And there'll you'd be, the only car'd be stopping in be someone that knows the area real well. Ah you'd definitely feel it, like. But you know. I get down here for a pint and that. There's a lot to be said for the company. And the . . . you know, the . . . someone there. Oh yeah.

VALERIE. Did you never consider it? When you were young.

JACK. Oh sure, yeah, of course I did, sure what the hell else does a youngfella be thinking about? You know? And Brendan knows. I had a girl, a lovely girl back then. We were courting for three years, and em, 1963 to '66. But she wanted to go up to Dublin, you know. She would have felt that that's what we should have done. And I don't know why it was a thing with me that I . . . an irrational fear, I suppose, that kept me here. And I couldn't understand why she wanted to be running off up to Dublin, you know? And she did in the end, anyway, like. And she was working up there waiting for me to come. But it was with me that it was like a mad thing, that I thought it was a thousand fucking miles away. Hated going up. I went up a few times like.

But . . . I was going up for . . . you know . . . she had a room. A freezing, damp place. I was a terrible fella. It became that that was the only thing I was going for. I couldn't stand being away. I don't know why. Ah I'd be all excited about going up for . . . the physical . . . the freedom of it. But after a day and a night, and I'd had my fill, we'd be walking in the park and I'd be all catty and bored, and moochy. (*Pause.*) Breaking the poor girl's heart. Ah, you get older and you look back on why you did things, you see that a lot of the time, there wasn't a reason. You do a lot of things out of pure cussedness. I stopped answering her letters. And I'd fucking dread one coming to the house. And her in it wondering how I was and was there something wrong with the post or this. (*Pause.*) I can't explain what carry on I was up to. I had just . . . left her out. Being the big fella, me dad handing over the business to me. Me swanning around. A man of substance. And then I had the gall to feel resentful when she wrote and said she was getting married to a fella.

Pause.

And I was all that it was her fault for going in the first place. Tss.

There was a delegation of people from all around here going up to the wedding on a bus. And I was just one of the crowd. Just one of the guests. In my suit, and the shoes nearly polished off me. And a hangover like you wouldn't believe. I'd been up 'til five or more, swilling this stuff, looking at the fire. And we were all on the bus at nine. And all the chat all around was why she hadn't come home to get married. And me sick as a dog. The smell of Brylcreem off all us culchies – sitting in the church in Phibsboro. All her lovely-looking nurse friends and their guard boyfriends. She was marrying a guard. Huge fella. Shoulders like a big gorilla. And they were going down the aisle after, and I caught her eye. And I gave her the cheesiest little grin you've ever seen. A little grin that was saying, 'Enjoy your big gorilla, 'cause the future's all ahead of me.'

And she just looked at me like I was only another guest at the wedding. And that was that. And the future *was* all ahead of me. Years and years of it. I could feel it coming. All those things you've got to face on your own. All by yourself. And you bear it 'cause you're showing everybody you're a great fella altogether. But I left the church like a little boy. And I walked away. I couldn't go to the reception. I just kept walking. There was a light rain. And then I was in town. It was a dark day. Like there was a roof on the city. And I found myself in a little labyrinth of streets. With nothing doing. And I ducked into a pub. Little dark place. Just one or two others there. A businesslike barman. Like yourself Brendan, ha?

Businesslike, dutiful. And I put a pint or two away. And a small one or two. And I sat there, just looking down at the dirty wooden bar. And the barman asked me if I was alright? Simple little question. And I said I was. And he said he'd make me a sandwich. And I said okay. And I nearly started crying – because you know, here was someone just . . . And I watched him. He took two big slices off a fresh loaf and buttered them carefully, spreading it all around. I'll never forget it. And then he sliced some cheese and cooked ham and an onion out of a jar, and put it all on a plate and sliced it down the middle. And, just someone doing this for me. And putting it down in front of me. 'Get that down you, now,' he said. And then he folded up his newspaper and put on his jacket, and went off on his break. And there was another barman then. And I took this sandwich up and I could hardly swallow it, because of the lump in my throat. But I ate it all down because someone I didn't know had done this for me. Such a small thing. But a huge thing. In my condition.

It fortified me, like no meal I ever had in my life. And I went to the reception. And I was properly ashamed of myself. There was a humility I've tried to find since. But goodness wears off. And it just gets easier to be a contrary bollocks.

Down in the garage. Spinning small jobs out all day. Taking hours to fix a puncture. Stops you thinking about what might of been and what you should have done. It's like looking away. Like I did at that reception. You should only catch someone's eye for the right reason.

But I do be at this fella, don't I? (*Pause.*)

Yep. (*Pause.*) I may be on my way now. (*Pause.*)

BRENDAN. Will you be alright in that wind?

JACK. Jaysus I should be used to that road by now, says you, ha?

BRENDAN. I'll get you the torch.

JACK. Am I a moaner?

BRENDAN (*going*). There's well fucking worse, I'll tell you.

Exits.

JACK. Well. That wasn't a ghostly story. Anyway, At least, ha?

VALERIE, No.

JACK. We've had enough of them. (*Pause.*) We'll all be ghosts soon enough, says you ha?

VALERIE. Mmm.

JACK. We'll all be sitting here. Sipping whiskey all night with Maura Nealon. (*Pause.*) Yeah. (*Short pause.*) This has been a strange little evening, for me.

VALERIE (*a little laugh*). For me as well.

JACK. Fuck, We could do worse. It was lovely to meet you.

VALERIE, You too.

JACK. Didn't mean to go on there.

VALERIE. No, please . . .

JACK. Something about your company. Inspiring, ha? And this of course. (*Glass.*)

They smile.

I wonder if being out here in the country is the best place for to . . . you know . . .

VALERIE. Why?

JACK. Ah. Girl like you. Hiding yourself away, Listening to old headers like us talking about the fairies. Having all your worst fears confirmed for you. Tuh. Ghosts and angels and all this? Fuck them. I won't have it. Because I won't see someone like you being upset by it. You've enough to deal with for fuck's sake. I am very, sorry, love, about what happened.

VALERIE. Thanks.

JACK (*standing up*). Makes you feel very powerless. I'll say that much.

BRENDAN *comes in turning the torch on and off.*

BRENDAN. The batteries are a bit weak. Come on I'll drop you.

JACK. Are you sure?

BRENDAN. Sure, I'm giving Valerie a lift.

VALERIE. Come with us.

JACK. Okay, then. Grand.

BRENDAN is clearing their glasses, going in behind the bar, tidying up.

VALERIE. Do you want a hand, Brendan?

BRENDAN. Oh no! Stay where you are, I'll be finished in a sec.

JACK takes his anorak, joking.

JACK. Is this yours, Valerie?

VALERIE. Yeah right.

JACK takes her jacket and holds it for her.

JACK. Come on.

VALERIE. Oh now. Very nice.

JACK. These are the touches, ha, Brendan?

BRENDAN. That's them.

JACK. Now.

VALERIE. Thanks.

JACK. Mmm. Have a last fag I think. (*Taking cigarette packet.*) Anyone else?

VALERIE. No, I won't thanks.

BRENDAN. No thanks, Jack.

JACK. Up early in the morning. Over to Conor Boland. He's over the other side of Carrick there. Has about fifteen fucking kids. Mmm.

Pause.

VALERIE. Will you be in here again soon?

JACK. Ah I'm always in and out. Got to keep the place afloat at least, you know?

BRENDAN (*working*). Don't mind him now, Valerie. Him and the Jimmy fella'll be fierce scarce around here the next few weeks.

VALERIE. Why?

BRENDAN (*stops work and lights a cigarette*). All the Germans'll be coming and they love it in here.

VALERIE (*to* JACK). You don't like that?

JACK makes a face.

BRENDAN. He thinks they're too noisy.

JACK. See, you don't know what they do be saying or anything.

BRENDAN. Him and Jimmy be sitting there at the bar with big sour pusses on them. Giving out like a couple of old grannies.

JACK. Ah we're not that bad.

BRENDAN. You're like a pair of bloody auld ones, you should see them.

VALERIE. Where do you go instead?

JACK. Ah, place down in Carrick, the Pot.

BRENDAN (*derision*). 'The Pot'. There does be just as many of them down there, don't be codding yourself.

JACK. Ah no, it doesn't seem as bad down there, now.

VALERIE. That's because this is your place.

JACK. Now. You've hit it on the head. You see, Brendan, Valerie's defending us. It's out of respect for this place.

BRENDAN. It is in my fucking barney, respect! The two of yous leaving me standing behind that bar with my arms folded picking my hole and not knowing what the hell is going on. And them playing all old sixties songs on their guitars. And they don't even know the words.

And nothing for me to do except pull a few pints and watch the shadow from the Knock moving along the floor, with the sun going down. I'm like some fucking mentaller, I do be watching it! Watching it creeping up on the Germans. And they don't even notice it.

I must be cracking up if that's my entertainment of an evening.

JACK. Ah don't be moaning. I'll tell you what. If Valerie's willing to come in and brave the Germans, then I'm sure me and Jim'll come in and keep yous company, how's that now?

BRENDAN. Oh you'll *grace* us with your ugly mushes, will you?

JACK. Don't push it, boy. Ah sure, Jaysus, what am I talking about? Sure you'll have Finbar in here sniffing around Valerie every night anyway.

VALERIE. Ah now stop.

They laugh a little.

JACK. He'll be like a fly on a big pile of shite, so he will. Jesus. That came out all wrong, didn't it?

BRENDAN. It certainly did, you big messer.

JACK. Couldn't have come out worse, sorry about that.

VALERIE. Would you relax?

BRENDAN is putting his jacket on.

JACK. Sorry. Will you anyway?

VALERIE. What? Come in . . . with the . . . Germans?

JACK. Yeah.

VALERIE. Doesn't bother me.

JACK. Ah, I think that's the right attitude. You should stay with the company and the bright lights.

BRENDAN. Do you see my keys?

He is looking around. VALERIE and JACK look around a little.

VALERIE. Sure I might even pick up some German.

JACK. Ah, I don't know. They're eh . . . Are they from Germany, Brendan?

BRENDAN. What?

JACK. The Germans. (*To* VALERIE.) We call them the Germans.

VALERIE picks keys off the mantelpiece.

VALERIE. Is this them?

BRENDAN. Yeah, thanks. Are we right?

They are moving towards the door.

JACK. Where are they from? Is it Denmark, or Norway? (*To* VALERIE.) It's somewhere like that.

JACK goes out, followed by VALERIE.

BRENDAN. Ah, I don't know where the fuck they're from.

BRENDAN turns off the light and leaves.